THOMAS HENRY HUXLEY

MODERN ENGLISH WRITERS.

Crown 8vo, 2/6 each.

READY.

MATTHEW ARNOLD . . .	Professor SAINTSBURY.
R. L. STEVENSON. . . .	L. COPE CORNFORD.
JOHN RUSKIN	Mrs MEYNELL.
ALFRED TENNYSON . . .	ANDREW LANG.
THOMAS HENRY HUXLEY .	EDWARD CLODD.
W. M. THACKERAY . . .	CHARLES WHIBLEY.
ROBERT BROWNING . . .	C. H. HERFORD.

IN PREPARATION.

GEORGE ELIOT	A. T. QUILLER-COUCH.
J. A. FROUDE	JOHN OLIVER HOBBES.

WILLIAM BLACKWOOD & SONS, EDINBURGH AND LONDON.

THOMAS HENRY HUXLEY

BY

EDWARD CLODD

Who saw life steadily, and saw it whole.
—Matthew Arnold.

SECOND IMPRESSION

WILLIAM BLACKWOOD AND SONS
EDINBURGH AND LONDON
MCMV

PREFATORY NOTE.

In the preparation of this book there have been large drafts from the materials supplied by Mr Leonard Huxley in the very admirable *Life and Letters* of his father. The footnote references to that work are sufficiently denoted by the omission of its title.

For the convenience of readers who may not possess the original editions of Huxley's writings, the references to them are, for the most part, cited from the *Collected Essays*.

CONTENTS.

CHRONOLOGY.

1825. Born at Ealing (4th May).

1841. Assistant to doctor at Rotherhithe.

1842. Student at Charing Cross Hospital Medical School.

1845. M.B. and Gold Medallist for Anatomy and Physiology at University of London.

1845. Discovered membrane of human hair known as " Huxley's layer."

1846. Entered Naval Medical Service.

1846. Appointed assistant-surgeon of the surveying ship Rattle-snake.

1849. Published memoir on the *Family of the Medusæ*.

1850. Returned to England : granted leave ashore to work out results of voyage.

1851. Elected Fellow of the Royal Society.

1852. Received Gold Medal of Royal Society.

1853. Further leave ashore refused : struck off the Navy List.

1853. Published article on the *Cell Theory*.

1854. Appointed Professor of Natural History and Palæontology in Royal School of Mines, and Curator of Fossils in Museum of Practical Geology.

1855. Married Henrietta Anne Heathorn, of Sydney.

1856. Visited Switzerland with Tyndall.

1857. Published paper on *The Structure and Motion of Glaciers*.

1857. Appointed Examiner in Physiology and Comparative Anatomy in University of London.

1857. Appointed Fullerian Professor of Comparative Anatomy at the Royal Institution.

1858. Appointed Croonian Lecturer.

1859. Published Croonian lecture on *Origin of the Vertebrate Skull.*

1859. Reviewed the *Origin of Species* in the *Times* (26th December).

1859. Appointed Secretary of the Geological Society.

1859. Published *Oceanic Hydrozoa.*

1860. Attended British Association Meeting at Oxford (debate with Bishop Wilberforce).

1861. Lectured on *Relation of Man to the rest of the Animal Kingdom* at Edinburgh and London.

1862. Elected Hunterian Professor at the Royal College of Surgeons.

1863. Published *Man's Place in Nature.*

1864. Appointed on Royal Commission on Sea Fisheries

> *Note.*—Huxley served between 1862 and 1884 on ten Royal Commissions on Fisheries, Scientific Education, &c.

1866. Received degree of LL.D. Edinburgh.

1866. Published *Lessons in Elementary Physiology.*

1868. Elected President of the Ethnological Society.

1868. Lectured on the *Physical Basis of Life.*

1868. Published memoirs on the *Classification of Birds* and on *Intermediate Animals between Birds and Reptiles.*

1869. Elected President of the Geological Society.

1869. Joined the Metaphysical Society.

1869. Published *Introduction to the Classification of Animals.*

1870. Elected President of British Association Meeting at Liverpool.

1870. Elected member of the first School Board for London.

1870. Published *Lay Sermons.*

1871. Appointed Secretary of the Royal Society.

1871. Broke down in health ; visited Egypt.

1872. Elected Lord Rector of Aberdeen University.

1873. Published *Critiques and Addresses.*

1874. Lectured on *Animals as Automata* at British Association Meeting, Belfast.

1874. Lectured on Natural History as deputy to Sir Wyville Thomson at Edinburgh.

1875. Took active part in controversy on Vivisection.

1875. Published *Practical Instruction in Elementary Biology.*

1876. Visited America.

1877. Published *American Addresses; Physiography;* and a *Manual of the Anatomy of Invertebrated Animals.*

1878. Published *Hume.*

1879. Received degree of LL.D. Cambridge.

1880. Lectured on *The Coming of Age of the 'Origin of Species'* at the Royal Institution.

1880. Published *The Crayfish;* an *Introduction to the Science of Zoology;* and *Introductory Science Primer.*

1881. Appointed Inspector of Salmon Fisheries.

1881. Became, on departmental changes at the School of Mines, Professor of Biology and Dean of the Royal College of Science.

1881. Published *Science and Culture.*

1883. Elected President of the Royal Society.

1883. Delivered the Rede Lecture at Cambridge (on *The Pearly Nautilus and Evolution*).

1884. Further breakdown in health.

1885. Received degree of D.C.L. Oxford.

1885. Retired on pension from all official appointments.

1886. Began series of papers on *Evolution of Theology.*

1888. Elected a Trustee of the British Museum.

1888. Received Copley Medal of the Royal Society.

1889. Removed to Eastbourne.

1891. Published *Social Diseases and Worse Remedies.*

1892. Published *Essays on Controverted Questions.*

1892. Made a Privy Councillor.

1893. Delivered Romanes Lecture at Oxford (on *Evolution and Ethics*).

1893-94. Reissued, with rearrangement, the articles and lectures in *Lay Sermons,* &c., in nine volumes entitled *Collected Essays.*

1894. Received Darwin Medal of the Royal Society.

1894. Attended British Association Meeting, Oxford.

1895. Died 29th June. Buried at Finchley, 4th July.

H U X L E Y.

———◆———

THE MAN.

THOMAS HENRY HUXLEY, the seventh and youngest child of George and Rachel Huxley, was born on the 4th May 1825, at Ealing, then a village separated by stretches of open country from London. His father, who was assistant-master in a semi-public school there, is described by him as a man "rather too easy-going for this wicked world," yet with a certain tenacity of character which, since he inherited it, Huxley dryly says, " unfriendly observers sometimes call obstinacy." This, together with a faculty for drawing, constituted the father's legacy to the son. It is of his mother that he declares himself "physically and mentally" the child, " even down to peculiar movements of the hands"; her agile mind, with its rapid arrival at conclusions, remained, he says, the perilous but most prized part of

his "inheritance of mother-wit." His love for her was
a passion.

But his boyhood was a cheerless time. Reversing
Matthew Arnold's sunnier memories :—

> No " rigorous teachers seized his youth,
> And purged its faith, and tried its fire,
> Shewed him the high, white star of truth,
> There bade him gaze, and there aspire."

He told Charles Kingsley that he was "kicked into
the world a boy without guide or training, or with
worse than none,"[1] and, contrasting Herbert Spencer's
happier lot, says that he "had two years of a Pande-
monium of a school (between eight and ten), and
after that neither help nor sympathy in any intellectual
direction till he reached manhood."[2]   On the dreary
week-days he was flung among boys of low type, and
on the drearier Sundays he was taken to church,
where the preacher's allusions to infidels left on his
mind the impression that "such folks belonged to the
criminal classes."   When he was about ten, the break-
up of the Ealing school sent the family, literally, to
Coventry, where, in the irony of fate, the shiftless
father became manager of a savings' bank.   The
daughters took to school-keeping, and the boys were
left free to browse among the remnants of the home
library.   Huxley was possessed of that love of reading which, in Gibbon's famous words, he "would not
have exchanged for the treasures of India."   From

[1] I. 220.   [2] II. 145.

boyhood to old age his tastes were omnivorous, rang-
ing from science and philosophy to the last new fiction.
Dr Johnson said that Burton's *Anatomy of Melancholy*
took him out of bed two hours before his usual time ;
Hutton's *Geology* kept Huxley in it, with blanket
pinned round his shoulders. At twelve he had read
Hamilton's essay *On the Philosophy of the Uncon-
ditioned*, with the result, he tells us, of stamping on
his mind "the strong conviction that on even the
most solemn and important of questions, men are apt to
take cunning phrases for answers." Carlyle's translations
from the German moved him to teach himself a language knowledge of which was to be of the utmost
service in his life-work. Of the influence which *Sartor
Resartus* had upon him, he says, "It led me to know
that a deep sense of religion was compatible with the
entire absence of theology."[1]

During this formative period his interests ranged from
speculations on the absolute basis of matter and the
crystallisation of carbon to the injustice of compelling
Dissenters to pay church rates. In the boy's quotation
from Lessing, "I hate all people who want to found
sects," there is the spirit of the man who said that
"science commits suicide when it adopts a creed." In
a scheme for a "classification of all knowledge" written
in a fragmentary journal, kept from his fifteenth to his
seventeenth year, there was the expression of that
passion for general principles, for search after unity at

[1] I. 220.

the core of things, which ruled all his observation and
speculation, and which is the salvation of a man from
the evil of specialism.

"Thus to be a Seeker is to be of the best sect next to
a Finder," said Oliver Cromwell; and of himself
Huxley, who at fifty-three learned Greek that he might
read Aristotle in the original, wrote three years before
his death, "I have always been, am, and propose to
remain a mere scholar." So wrote Michael Angelo in
old age, "Imparo ancora"—I am learning still.

Huxley's bent, like that, it may be added, of both
Herbert Spencer and the late W. B. Carpenter, was
towards mechanical engineering, and this was manifest
in his life-work. For his interest centred in the "archi-
tectural part" of organisms, in the adaptation of
apparatus to function, and in whatever evidenced
"unity of plan in the thousands and thousands of
diverse living constructions."[1] Whatever he worked
at, he "visualised clearly" by diagram or map or
picture.

He paid a lifelong penalty for his curiosity about the
mechanism of the human body. When he was fourteen
he was taken by some student friends to a post-mortem,
the result of which was an attack of blood-poisoning.
To this he attributed the "hypochondriacal dyspepsia"
which afflicted him to the end of his life. Although
engineering was his hobby, medicine, at the start, was
his destiny. At sixteen, on the removal of his family

[1] I. 7.

to Rotherhithe, he was placed as assistant to a Dr Chandler as a preliminary to "walking the hospitals." Many of the patients were in more need of food than physic, a condition of things which set Huxley wondering "why the masses did not sally forth and get a few hours' eating and drinking and plunder to their heart's content before the police could stop and hang a few of them." [1]

This early contact with the grim realities of the social problem gave him authority to be heard upon the economic and educational questions in which his interest deepened with his years, and to indicate to the people how they may alone work out their own salvation.

I believe in the fustian [he said], and can talk to it better than to any amount of gauze and Saxony. . . . I want the working classes to understand that Science and her ways are great facts for them—that physical virtue is the base of all other, and that they are to be clean and temperate and all the rest—not because fellows in black with white ties tell them so, but because these are plain and patent laws of nature which they must obey under penalties.[2]

Leaving Mr Chandler, he was apprenticed to his brother-in-law, Dr Scott (Huxley's two sisters had married doctors), and began study for the matriculation examination of the University of London. He failed in this, but had compensation in winning the silver medal of the Pharmaceutical Society, while the standard

[1] I. 16.   [2] I. 138.

reached by his brother James and himself secured them free scholarships in the medical school of Charing Cross Hospital. In 1845 he passed his M.B. at the University of London and made his first discovery in detecting a hitherto unknown membrane at the root of the human hair. It is known as "Huxley's layer." The next year he acted on the suggestion of a fellow-student, Mr (now Sir Joseph) Fayrer, and applied to Sir William Burnet, then Director of the Medical Service, for a naval appointment. Sir William returned his visiting card "with the frugal reminder" that he might "probably find it useful on some other occasion," but the interview gained him entry on the books of Nelson's old ship, the Victory, for duty at Haslar Hospital. Then came a turn of the tide which, not without ebb, led on to fortune, at least to the fortune—never, despite the discreditable insinuation in *Punch*,[1] a commercial one— which Huxley coveted.

Owen Stanley, son of the Bishop of Norwich and brother of Dean Stanley, was in command of the Rattlesnake, a 28-gun frigate commissioned to survey the intricate passages within the barrier-reef skirting the eastern shores of Australia, between which colony and the mother country a shorter sea-passage was demanded by the growing trade. Captain Stanley wanted an assistant-surgeon, and on the recommendation of Sir John Richardson, the famous Arctic explorer, Huxley was given the post. It was the best possible appren-

[1] II. 26.

ticeship for the work which lay, unsuspected, before him—the solution of the problems of organology, and the indicating of their far-reaching significance. Life had its origin in water, and therein the biologist finds his most suggestive material. Darwin and Joseph Hooker had passed through a like curriculum—the one in 1831, the other in 1839.

The Rattlesnake left Plymouth on the 12th December 1846, two years before Bates and Wallace sailed for exploration of the Amazons. It was a time of preparation, each only vaguely knowing to what ends he worked, but in his measure contributing answer to the question whether species were mutable or permanent.

The conditions on board the Rattlesnake contrasted ill with the luxurious equipment of exploring ships since her time. She was a man-of-war of the old class; her seams were leaky; the berths swarmed with cockroaches, and the biscuits with weevils. The Admiralty refused to supply any books, and in the absence of proper apparatus for sifting the contents of the dredge, Huxley had to adapt a wire meat-cover. The ship carried an official naturalist, whose chief care was to collect objects for museums, leaving to Huxley's willing hands the dissection and examination of the specimens brought up from the deep sea.

The first long stay was made at Sydney, where Huxley met his future wife, Henrietta Annie Heathorn. For her he was "to serve longer and harder than Jacob thought to serve for Rachel," of whom, in immortal words, the poet-chronicler says, "seven years seemed unto him but a few days for the love he had to her." [1] Huxley had his reward in forty years of the closest and most helpful fellowship.

The nature and import of the work accomplished by him during the voyage, which came to an end in November 1849, will be dealt with in the next chapter. Here it suffices to say that while sundry reports on marine creatures, which were sent to the Linnean Society, were pigeon-holed, better fortune attended a paper on the Medusæ or jelly-fish family, transmitted to the Royal Society through Bishop Stanley, whose admirable *History of Birds* has survived his episcopal charges. It was promptly published, and was the warrant of Huxley's election into the Society at the early age of twenty-six. Thus far he could have no quarrel with bishops.

Back in England, "equipped as a perfect zoologist and keen-sighted ethnologist" (the words are Virchow's), Huxley obtained for a time the privilege of appointment for "particular service," which enabled him to work out on shore the results of the voyage. But nearly five years of suspense and struggle were to pass before he secured a permanent appointment of £200 per annum, one-half of the modest maximum he desired. Writing to his sister in 1850 he says :—

I have no ambition, except as means to an end, and that end is the possession of a sufficient income to marry upon.

---

[1] Genesis xxix. 20.

. . . A worker I must always be—it is my nature—but if I had £400 a-year I would never let my name appear to anything I did or ever shall do. It would be glorious to be a voice working in secret, and free from all those personal motives that have actuated the best.[1]

He was in the front rank of anatomists; in 1852 his society conferred upon him the Royal Medal, which, for the £50 worth of gold therein, he sold eleven years after, to assist a brother's widow; he was deluged with invitations to dinners and soirées while not earning enough to pay his cab-fare. He kept fragile body and self-reliant soul together by writing, lecturing, and translating. Toronto, Aberdeen, Cork, King's College, each in turn rejected him as he sought a professorship of natural history, and he had thoughts of trying his luck as a doctor in Australia, if only to be near his sweetheart. Domestic cares, his mother's death, and his father's serious illness, added to the gloom of these five dreary years. But though his circumstances ran low, his ideals soared high. In the letter of 1850 to his sister he says :—

I don't know and I don't care whether I shall ever be what is called a great man. I will leave my mark somewhere, and it shall be clear and distinct—

T. H. H. his mark—

and free from the abominable blur of cant, humbug, and self-seeking which surrounds everything in this present world—that is to say, supposing that I am not already unconsciously tainted myself, a result of which I have a morbid dread.[2]

---

[1] I. 62.　　　　　　　　[2] I. 63.

At the end of 1853 the Admiralty commanded him
to join the ship Illustrious; he refused, and paid the
penalty in being struck off the Navy List. But, as he
cheerily said, "there is always a Cape Horn in one's
life," and, "not without a good deal of damage to spars
and rigging," he rounded it. In July 1854, on the
transfer of his friend Edward Forbes to Edinburgh, he
was appointed Professor of Natural History at the
School of Mines with a salary of £200, which, soon
after, was doubled on his becoming naturalist to the
Geological Survey. The next year Miss Heathorn's
parents brought her to England. Her health was so
bad that a famous doctor gave her only six months
to live. But the faculty differed; Huxley took the
brighter view, and wrote thus to Hooker on the 11th
July:—

I terminate my Baccalaureate and take my degree of
M.A.trimony (isn't that atrocious?) on Saturday, July 21.

When he was appointed to the School of Mines he
told Sir Henry De la Beche that he "didn't care for
fossils," the mechanism of the living animal alone interesting him. But it came to pass that during his
thirty-one years' tenure of his post the larger part of
his work was palæontological. And well that this so
happened, because, when the battle over organic evolution was fought, Huxley was able to adduce out of his
treasury of knowledge a mass of evidence from the
fossil-yielding rocks which, supplemented by the evi-

dence from embryology, put the theory of "descent with modification" on a foundation which cannot be shaken.

Routine work leaves little, if any, time for original investigation. Administrative detail filled the larger part of each day with Huxley; his heart was centred in schemes for the diffusion of science; the arrangement and cataloguing of the contents of the Jermyn Street Museum was a labour of years; he gave, ungrudgingly, help in forming other public as well as private collections, which, in his own words,

should be large enough to illustrate the most important truths of natural history, but not so extensive as to weary and confuse ordinary visitors.

But with Huxley this, although an essential, was a secondary, part of the business; with the organising of materials there went *pari passu* instruction in their nature and meaning, involving courses of lectures and series of articles, both technical and popular, while other public appointments made their inroads on his time. This would seem enough to exhaust the day, and when it is remembered that all which he undertook, paid and unpaid alike, was done despite frequent breakdown from dyspepsia and allied troubles, the marvel grows that he found a moment for original research, or for the wide and varied reading which, fortifying him on every side, enabled him "to put to flight the armies" of the obscurantists in science, ethics, and theology.

Work was his passion, method was his salvation; he

took care of the minutes and the hours took care of
themselves. And yet, like Gibbon, who wrote—

While every one looks on me as a prodigy of application, I
know myself how strong a propensity I have to indolence,

we find Huxley accusing himself of an ingrained lazi-
ness.[1]

On the last night of 1856, while waiting for the birth
of his first child, he made this entry in his journal :—

1856-7-8 must still be " Lehrjahre" to complete training
in principles of Histology, Morphology, Physiology, Zoology, and Geology by *Monographic Work* in each department. 1860 will then see me well grounded and ready for
any special pursuits in either of these branches. . . . In
1860 I may fairly look forward to fifteen or twenty years'
" Meisterjahre"; and with the comprehensive views my
training will give me, I think it will be possible in that time
to give a new and healthier direction to all Biological Science.
To smite all humbugs, however big, to give a nobler tone to
science ; to set an example of abstinence from petty personal
controversies, and of toleration for everything but lying ; to
be indifferent as to whether the work is recognised as mine
or not, so long as it is done : are these my aims ? 1860 will
show.
Half-past ten at night. Waiting for my child. I seem to
fancy it the pledge that all these things shall be.
Born five minutes before twelve. Thank God. New-
Year's Day, 1857.[2]

On the 20th September 1860, a year that was to
" show " so much, there was made the last entry in the
journal, telling what lifelong sorrow fell upon a great
and tender soul.

[1] I. 268.   [2] I. 151.

And the same child, our Noel, our first-born, after being
for nearly four years our delight and our joy, was carried off
by scarlet fever in forty-eight hours. This day week he and
I had a great romp together. On Friday his restless head,
with its bright blue eyes and tangled golden hair, tossed all
day upon his pillow. On Saturday night, the fifteenth, I
carried him here into my study, and laid his cold still body
here where I write. Here too, on Sunday night, came his
mother and I to that holy leave-taking.

My boy is gone; but in a higher and better sense than
was in my mind when I wrote four years ago what stands
above, I feel that my fancy has been fulfilled. I say heartily,
and without bitterness—Amen, so let it be.[1]

In a very remarkable letter, written at this time to
Charles Kingsley in reply to one setting forth the warrant for belief in immortality, the attitude of Huxley
from his youth upwards towards the current theology
is shown clearly.[2] He sees no justification for the
belief; the arguments in its favour are to his mind
"delusive and mischievous," and there, since his was
not the spirit which denies, he leaves the matter. The
letter contains the already-quoted remark that *Sartor
Resartus* led him to knowledge of the non-dependence
of religion on theology, religion meaning, as he says
elsewhere, simply the reverence and love for the ethical
ideal, and the desire to realise that ideal in life, which
every man ought to feel.[3] He adds :—

Science and her methods gave me a resting-place independent of authority and tradition. Love opened up to me
a view of the sanctity of human nature, and impressed me
with a deep sense of responsibility.

[1] I. 152. [2] I. 217-222. [3] *Collected Essays*, v. p. 249.

In the chapter on "The Everlasting No" in *Sartor*, Carlyle had said :—

After all the nameless woes that Inquiry, which for me, what it is not always, was genuine love of Truth, had wrought me, I nevertheless still loved Truth and bate no jot of my allegiance to her.

In that allegiance Huxley never wavered :—

If wife and child, and name and fame were all lost to me, one after another, still I would not lie. . . . The longer I live, the more obvious it is to me that the most sacred act of a man's life is to say and to feel, "I believe such and such to be true." All the greatest rewards and all the heaviest penalties of existence cling about that act. The universe is one and the same throughout ; and if the condition of my success in unravelling some little difficulty of anatomy or physiology is, that I shall rigorously refuse to put faith in that which does not rest on sufficient evidence, I cannot believe that the great mysteries of existence will be laid open to me on other terms.[1]

Huxley summed up the whole matter in his Rectorial Address to the students of Aberdeen University : "Veracity is the heart of morality." His references to the formative influences on his life in the letter to Kingsley are prefaced by the statement that his neglected boyhood had been followed by a profligate manhood. His words are, "I confess to my shame that few men have drank deeper of all kinds of sin than I." Commenting on this in his review of the *Life and Letters*, Sir W. Thiselton-Dyer says, "Frankly, I do not believe a word of it."

---

[1] I. 217.

And those who knew Huxley in any degree of intimacy will agree with him. Sir W. Thiselton-Dyer adds :—

> In a rather serious conversation I once had with him, he spoke of a period in his life when he *might* have taken to evil courses ; but he did not give me the smallest reason to suppose that in the retrospect he saw more than the existence of a possible *crevasse* in his path into which he might have fallen.[1]

The truth is that we have here the language of exaggeration born of the desolation of the moment; the "troops of follies and errors"[2] of youth refracted through the medium of tears. It is the language of Augustine's *Confessions*; of Bunyan's *Grace Abounding*; and of the

> many excellent persons whose moral character from boyhood to old age has been free from any stain discernible to their fellow-creatures, who have, in their autobiographies or diaries, applied to themselves, and doubtless with sincerity, epithets as severe as could be applied to Titus Oates or Mrs Brownrigg.[3]

In acknowledging a birthday letter from one of his daughters, Huxley hopes that his own imperfections may make him deal the more gently with those of others. He adds that he has little toleration for the "just man who needed no repentance," and whose smugly correct family circle "was perhaps as the interior of an ice-pail."[4] Walter Bagehot remarks that "in the greatest cases scientific men have been calm men. There is a coldness in their fame. We think of Euclid as of pure ice ;

[1] *Nature*, 13th June 1901, p. 146. [2] II. 330.
[3] Macaulay's *Essays*, "John Bunyan," iv. p. 407. [4] II. 331.

we admire Newton as we admire the Peak of Teneriffe." [1]
The statement is too sweeping; it has no application to
Huxley, in whom was neither coldness nor detachment.
He was hot-tempered; now and again he was austere to
a degree approaching severity : he had, as with all strong
individualities, strong likes and dislikes.[2] But the
anger and the austerity were passing moods; they were
the price which he and others paid for abiding virtues;
for the "woman's element"[3] in him which made him
cling to wife and children; for the quick response to
every call of duty or affection; for the generous application of great powers to noble and unselfish ends. Of
him may be said what Lowell has said of Lessing : "No
biographical chemistry is needed to bleach spots out of
his reputation."[4] His home was "a focus of the best
affections not less than of intellectual light."[5] He loved
anniversaries; the devotion of his children warmed him
"better than the sun," and when his gifted daughter
Marian died in the flower of womanhood, he confessed,
in the depth of his grief, that "man is not a rational
animal, especially in his parental capacity." Where he
hated, the scorn and loathing were deserved, for they
were manifest only against the insincere and the evasive;
if he could not brook contradiction, it was only where
ignorance or folly vaunted their assurance and their

---

[1] *Literary Studies*, ii. p. 222.   [2] II. 409.

[3] "I have a woman's element in me."—I. 61.

[4] *The English Poets and other Essays*, p. 278.

[5] Leslie Stephen, on "Huxley," *Nineteenth Century*, Dec. 1900,
p. 917.

blunders; if he could not suffer bores gladly, by what right did they compel a waste of time ungrudgingly given where counsel or information were honestly asked, no matter by whom? For, like all men who loom large in the public eye, he had to make enforced acquaintance with that aggravated variety of the species known as the crank. Circle - squarers and earth - flatteners pestered him with pamphlets; four-paged letters praying for his conversion, or, more often, for his damnation, as an atheist of the most mischievous type, were sent to him; bulky manuscripts, crammed with mad theories, which he was asked to revise and get published, were left at his house. Sometimes the comic side of the matter appealed to him, as witness this note to his friend Sir John Donnelly:—

I had a letter from a fellow yesterday morning who must be a lunatic, to the effect that he had been reading my essays, thought I was just the man to spend a month with, and was coming down by the five o'clock train, attended by his seven children and his *mother-in-law !*

Frost being over, there was lots of boiling water ready for him, but he did not turn up !

Wife and servants expected nothing less than assassination ! [1]

The entry in his journal, " 1860 will show," had deeper significance than Huxley dreamed when he made it. In 1858, he had delivered a lecture on the origin of the vertebrate skull, in which he demolished a theory propounded by Oken, supported by Goethe, and indorsed

[1] II. 372.

by Owen. At that time the influence of Owen in biological science was supreme and unchallenged, and it
needed no small courage to tell so high an authority
that even he might sometimes be in error. Moreover,
the task was not easier when, as experience showed,
Owen was no fair fighter, and given to sacrificing truth
to expediency.

As Huxley cared nothing for authority, and everything for truth, it is not surprising that the result was
an "internecine feud" between them. The breach was
widened on the publication of the *Origin of Species;*
an event which, in Huxley's words, "marks the Hejira
of Science from the idolatries of special creation to
the purer faith of Evolution."[1] In a paper on the
*Characters, Principles of Division, and Primary Groups
of the Class Mammalia*, read by Owen before the
Linnean Society in 1859, he referred to certain cerebral
structures as "peculiar to the genus Homo," and added
that the "peculiar mental powers associated with this
highest form of brain" warranted the placing of man in
a distinct sub-class of the Mammalia.

At the meeting of the British Association at Oxford
on 28th June 1860, Owen emphasised the statement
that "the brain of the gorilla presented more differences,
as compared with the brain of man, than it did when
compared with the brains of the very lowest and most
problematical of the Quadrumana." To this Huxley, in

[1] Review of Haeckel's *Anthropogenie. Academy,* 2nd January
1875.

polite English, gave the lie direct, and pledged himself
to "justify that unusual procedure elsewhere."[1] Two
days after, by mere chance, he was present at the
reading of a paper by Dr Draper *On the Intellectual
Development of Europe considered with reference to the
views of Mr Darwin*. In the discussion which followed,
Bishop Wilberforce, throwing a glance at Huxley, ended
a suave and superficial speech by asking him "as to his
belief in being descended from an ape. Is it on his
grandfather's or his grandmother's side that the ape ancestry comes in?" Huxley did not rise till the meeting
called for him; then he let himself go.[2] "The Lord
hath delivered him into mine hands," he said in under-
tone to Sir Benjamin Brodie. After showing how ill-
equipped was the Bishop for controversy upon the
general question of organic evolution, although it was
an open secret that Owen had primed him for the contest, Huxley said: "You say that development drives
out the Creator, but you assert that God made you;
and yet you know that you yourself were originally a little
piece of matter, no bigger than the end of this gold
pencil-case?" Then followed the famous retort :—

I asserted, and I repeat, that a man has no reason to be
ashamed of having an ape for his grandfather. If there
were an ancestor whom I should feel shame in recalling it
would rather be a *man*—a man of restless and versatile
intellect—who, not content with success in his own sphere of

---

[1] *Man's Place in Nature*, p. 114 (1863 edition).
[2] Letter to F. Darwin, i. p. 187.

activity, plunges into scientific questions with which he has no real acquaintance, only to obscure them by an aimless rhetoric, and distract the attention of his hearers from the real point at issue by eloquent digressions and skilled appeals to religious prejudice.[1]

The rebuke was supplemented in an article in the *Natural History Review*, January 1861, on the "Zoological Relation of Man with the Lower Animals," wherein Huxley redeemed his promise to refute Owen, and proved that "the brains of the lower true apes and monkeys differ far more widely from the brain of the orang than the brain of the orang differs from that of man."[2]

Whether [he says], as some think, man is, by his origin, distinct from all other living beings, or whether, on the other hand, as others suppose, he is the result of the modification of some other mammal, his duties and his aspirations must, I apprehend, remain the same. The proof of his claim to independent parentage will not change the brutishness of man's lower nature ; nor, except to those valet souls who cannot see greatness in their fellow because his father was a cobbler, will the demonstration of a pithecoid pedigree one whit diminish man's divine right of kingship over nature ; nor lower the great and princely dignity of perfect manhood, which is an order of nobility, not inherited, but to be won by each of us, so far as he consciously seeks good and avoids evil, and puts the faculties with which he is endowed to their fittest use.[3]

Notwithstanding "the crushing evidence from original dissections of numerous apes' brains" adduced by Rol-

[1] There is a good portrait of Huxley at this time in *Reminiscences of Oxford*, by Rev. W. Tuckwell.

[2] P. 84.   [3] *Ib.*, p. 67.

leston, Flower, and other comparative anatomists, Owen repeated and never retracted the thing which he must have known to be false : the question between Huxley and himself therefore became one of " personal veracity," and led to a permanent rupture. Moreover, Owen was known to have written an adverse notice of the *Origin of Species* in the *Edinburgh Review* of April 1860, and to have inspired Wilberforce in the preparation of his article upon the book in the *Quarterly Review* of the following July, an article of which Huxley said—

It is a production which should be bound up in good stout calf, or better, asses' skin, if such material is to be had, by the curious book-collector, together with Brougham's attack on the undulatory theory of light when it was first propounded by Young.

The outcome of all this was his first, and, in many respects, his most important book, *Evidence as to Man's Place in Nature*, which, based upon lectures delivered to working men in London, and at the Philosophical Institution of Edinburgh, was published in 1863. He was no superficial student of his kind ; he was anthropologist as well as anatomist ; he had studied in the book of the world more than in the world of books. As he told an audience in 1882, it had been his fate

to be familiar with almost every form of society, from the uncivilised savage of Papua and Australia and the civilised savages of the slums and dens of the poverty-stricken parts of great cities, to those who, perhaps, are occasionally the somewhat over-civilised members of our upper ten thousand.[1]

---

[1] *Coll. Essays*, iii. p. 164.

He saw with Herbert Spencer and Darwin (who had been content to throw out a bare hint at the end of his book) that if the processes of what is called the law of Evolution are applicable anywhere, they are applicable everywhere; that when once the fundamental relation of man to the lower animals, so far as his bodily structure and functions are concerned, is proven, inquiry into the relation of his mental apparatus and faculties to theirs must follow, and, with this, the study of his intellectual and spiritual development, and of his progress from the selfishness of the primitive horde to the comity of nations.   Hence, as he says in the second division of the book—

The question of questions for mankind—the problem which underlies all others, and is more deeply interesting than any other—is the ascertainment of the place which Man occupies in nature and of his relation to the universe of things. Whence our race has come; what are the limits of our power over nature and of nature's power over us; to what goal we are tending; are the problems which present themselves anew and with undiminished interest to every man born into the world.[1]

While, however, this interest in ultimate problems, evidenced in the journal of his boyhood, grew with his years, it absorbed no undue proportion of his time. Man in his relation to his fellows had more interest for him, and explains Huxley's activities in all things affecting the body politic, and the social progress of his kind. Needless to say that he who was all for truth was like-

[1] P. 56.

wise all for freedom.   In 1862, when the Civil War in America was raging, and when Gladstone was telling us that Jefferson Davis had "made a nation," Huxley never doubted that slavery was doomed.   Not that he believed in the negro ; he knew how permanent are the natural inequalities of races, and how hopeless, except in the rarest cases, it is to look for any elevation of the sensuous and volatile black, charged as he is with animal instincts accumulated beneath the tropical suns of unnumbered years.   But he was for the North, because "slavery means bad political economy, bad social morality, and a bad influence upon free labour and freedom all over the world."[1]   Two years later, he joined the Jamaica Committee, formed to prosecute Governor Eyre for the execution of the negro Gordon, because "English law does not permit good persons as such to strangle bad persons, as such."[2]

He was in favour of the emancipation of women, of the removal of every obstacle in the way of their intellectual advancement and development.[3]   Writing to Miss Jex Blake about her difficulty in obtaining a medical education, he said

that he was at a loss to understand on what grounds of justice or public policy, a career which is open to the weakest and most foolish of the male sex should be forcibly closed to women of vigour and capacity.

---

[1] I. 252.   In like manner, Darwin, writing at this time to Asa Gray, says : " Great God ! how I should like to see the greatest curse on earth—slavery—abolished ! "—*Life and Letters*, ii. p. 375.
[2] I. 280.   [3] I. 212.

They should, if they so pleased,

become merchants, barristers, politicians. Let them have
a fair field, but let them understand, as the necessary correlative, that they are to have no favour.   Let Nature alone sit
high above the lists, "rain influence and judge the prize."

But the prize, he was sure, would not be theirs, since the
most Darwinian of theorists will not venture to propound the
doctrine that the physical disabilities under which women
have hitherto laboured in the struggle for existence with men
are likely to be removed by even the most skilfully conducted
process of educational selection.[1]

Strongly convinced, as the most pronounced indi-
vidualist can be, that it is desirable that every man
should be free to act in every way which does not
limit the corresponding freedom of his fellow-man, he
made his practical protest against the liberty-infringing
Deceased Wife's Sister Bill in approving the union of
one of his daughters with the husband of her late sister
Marian.   And while knowing, as few knew so well,
what an "immense amount of remediable misery exists
among us," misery which, "if not effectually dealt with,
will destroy modern civilisation," he opposed the means
adopted by the Salvation Army to cope with it, not
because of its "Corybantic Christianity" and coarse
dogmas, but because a fanatical despotism controls it.

Few social evils are of greater magnitude than unin-
structed and unchastened religious fanaticism ; no personal
habit more surely degrades the conscience and the intellect
than blind and unhesitating obedience to unlimited autho-

---

[1] *Lay Sermons*, p. 22.

rity. Undoubtedly, harlotry and intemperance are sore evils, and starvation is hard to bear, or even to know of; but the prostitution of the mind, the soddening of the conscience, the dwarfing of manhood, are worse calamities.[1]

By the time that *Evidence as to Man's Place in Nature* was written, Huxley had command of a style which, in the judgement of Sir Spencer Walpole, — a judgement with which few will be found to disagree,— "made him the greatest master of prose of his time."[2] Apt in application to him is Caxton's tribute to Chaucer, "for he writeth no void words, but all his matter is full of high and quick sentence." Yet with a great price bought he this freedom of ready speech and pen. Those who heard, and, hearing, can never forget, his wonderful discourse *On the Coming of Age of the Origin of Species*, at the Royal Institution in 1880, when, without notes, he told the story of that epoch-making book in clear and forceful English which held his audience spellbound, may learn with surprise that his early essays upon the platform boded ill for his success. But he, who all the days of his life was at school, profited by criticism of the kind which came from a local institute, begging "not to have that young man again"; from working men; and from members of the Royal Institution. As a writer, he had served a useful apprenticeship in reviewing and popular "pot-boiling, whereby there is acquired the art of condensation and simplification of a subject"; while a retentive memory

[1] *Coll. Essays*, ix. p. 244.　　　　[2] II. 25.

utilised the stores of years of miscellaneous reading in his own and other languages for example and allusion.

But all this would have availed little in the absence of that mother-wit which gave him quick insight into things ; and of that passion for logical symmetry whereby he made clear to others what he saw clearly himself. He followed methods, not models ; he "doubted the wisdom of attempting to mould one's style by any other process than that of striving after the clear and forcible expression of definite conceptions." In commending the study of Hobbes for dignity, of Swift for concision and clearness, and of Defoe and Goldsmith for simplicity,[1] he commended the qualities with which his own work is charged. *Ars est celare artem*, and deftly enough has he effaced the traces of the labour which the preparation of his lectures and his writing cost him. In 1860 he wrote to Hooker, "It becomes more and more difficult to me to *finish* things satisfactorily " ;[2] and thirty years after, in a letter to M. de Varigny, he says :—

I have a great love and respect for my native tongue [that " noble instrument of thought," he elsewhere calls it], and take great pains to use it properly. Sometimes I write essays half-a-dozen times before I can get them into the proper shape, and I believe I become more fastidious as I grow older." [3]

The nine volumes of *Collected Essays* bear evidence throughout to Huxley's supreme skill as an interpreter,

[1] II. 284 ; and see *Coll. Essays*, vi. p. xii.
[2] I. 215.   [3] II. 291.

and to his genius for constructing while he demolished. Miscellaneous as are their contents, they have the unity which is inspired by a central idea. With the exception of a verbal correction, and of a slightly qualifying foot-note, here and there, each stands as it was originally written. Revision could only have impaired their stately, lucid, and sonorous prose, while to their main subject - matter all subsequent additions to knowledge have brought only confirmation.

As for his letters, with which his son has, wisely, largely filled his biography, even where traces of hurry may be noted, there is never a slovenly sentence; the gist of an essay is often packed in a few lines, and the passion to put things in such a way that the meaning may be seen at a glance is as apparent as in the more elaborate compositions. And the humorous touches, sparsely, but always effectively, applied in these, are, in the letters to friends and familiars, thrown in freely, with a boy-like enjoyment of the fun.

In the limits of a sketch which permits only of an attempt to portray the salient features of Huxley's character, and to indicate his attitude towards the burning questions of his time, confusion rather than clearness would result from import of details of the less eventful years. Hence the sometimes abrupt passage from one period to another, leaving the blanks to be filled up by reference to the brief chronological table which precedes this outline.

In 1870, perhaps the busiest year of Huxley's busy life, he was urged to offer himself as a candidate for the newly-formed School Board for London. His many commitments made him hesitate to stand, but he consented, because the position gave him a coveted chance of helping to put into practice the theories of education which he had long advocated. The opportunity was given him ; he came out second on the poll. His views upon the subject are scattered through many lectures and essays, but their consistency permits brief presentment. He contended that education should be "free and equal"; the business of the school boards being the provision of "a ladder reaching from the gutter to the university, along which every child in the three kingdoms should have the chance of climbing as far as he was fit to go."[1] That the race is to the swift and the battle to the strong, was added reason for according equality of opportunity : Nature might be depended upon to let the incompetent find their level. In *physical* training, drill and the simpler kind of gymnastics should be taught, the importance of this being paramount in the case of town-bred children who, shut up in sunless alleys, have to amuse themselves with "marbles and chuck-farthings instead of cricket or hare-and-hounds." He would have girls taught the elements of household work, if a supply of competent servants and of thrifty housewives is to be maintained. In *mental* training, after the "three R's," reading being taught so

[1] *Coll. Essays*, iii. p. 424.

as to make it a pleasure and incentive, foremost place should be given to some one or more of the natural sciences, because these bring the faculties of observation and inquiry into play, and because, in teaching a child the nature and properties of things, he is shown that the method of reaching knowledge of these is to be applied to every other branch of knowledge.

Let every child be instructed in those general views of the phenomena of Nature for which we have no exact English name. The nearest approximation to a name for what I mean, and which we possess, is "physical geography."[1] The Germans have a better, *Erdkunde* ("earth knowledge" or "geology" in its etymological sense), that is to say, a general knowledge of the earth, and what is on it, in it, and about it. The child asks, "What is the moon, and why does it shine?" "What is this water, and where does it run?" "What is the wind?" "What makes the waves in the sea?" "Where does this animal live, and what is the use of that plant?" And if not snubbed and stunted by being told not to ask foolish questions, there is no limit to the intellectual craving of a young child; nor any bounds to the slow, but solid, accretion of knowledge and development of the thinking faculty in this way. To all such questions, answers which are necessarily incomplete, though true as far as they go, may be given by any teacher whose ideas represent real knowledge and not mere book-learning; and a panoramic view of Nature, accompanied by a strong infusion of the scientific habit of mind, may thus be placed within the reach of every child of nine or ten.[2]

Huxley deemed it necessary for everybody, whether

[1] The more inclusive, but somewhat indefinite, term "physio-graphy," has since come into use.

[2] *Lay Sermons*, p. 55.

for a longer or shorter period, to learn to draw—a thing
quite feasible, since everybody can be taught to write,
and writing is a form of drawing. The value of this
cannot be

exaggerated, because it gives the means of training the
young in attention and accuracy, the two things in which
all mankind are more deficient than in any other mental
quality whatever.[1]

Among scientific topics he would include the

elements of the theory of political and social life, which,
strangely enough, it never seems to occur to anybody to
teach a child.   I would have the history of our own country,
and of all the influences which have been brought to bear
upon it, with incidental geography, taught, not as a mere
chronicle of reigns and battles, not as evidence that Providence has always been on the side of the Whigs or Tories,
but as a chapter in the development of the race, and the
history of civilisation.[2]

Literature should have a large place, because

an exclusively scientific training will bring about a mental
twist as surely as an exclusively literary training.   For
literature is the greatest of all sources of refined pleasure,
and there is scope enough for the purposes of liberal education in the study of the rich treasures of our own language
alone. . . . I have said before, and I repeat it here, that if
a man cannot get literary culture of the highest kind out of
his Bible, and Chaucer, and Shakespeare, he cannot get it
out of anything, and I would assuredly devote a very large
portion of the time of every English child to the careful
study of models of English writing of such varied and
wonderful kind as we possess, and, what is still more im-

---

[1] *Coll. Essays*, iii. p. 183.   [2] *Ib.*, iii. p. 184.

portant, and still more neglected, the habit of using that
language with precision, with force, and with art.[1]

These, together with translations of the best ancient
and modern works, where time or circumstance do not
permit of the learning of foreign languages, Huxley
counted among the essentials. The law of proportion, *non multa, sed multum*, must be observed if there
is to be any thoroughness in education, and if the
freshness and vigour of body and mind are to be
maintained, as they can be only by avoidance of "the
educational abomination of desolation of the present
day—the stimulation of young people to work at high
pressure by incessant competitive examinations."[2]

A generation has passed since these words were
written, and things remain as they were. Education,
whether in public or elementary school, is as bad as it
can be. It belies its name. There is no "drawing-
out," but only a cramming-in ; no cultivation of observation, of reasoning, or reflection ; only the teaching of
a crowd of facts without making clear their relation,
and hence no incitement to independent thought.

Technical training, the importance of which Huxley
enforced in a remarkable essay on 'The Struggle for
Existence in Human Society,'[3] he left to the workshop,
"as the only real school for a handicraft."

In *moral* training ; since each child is
a member of a social and political organisation of great

---

[1] *Coll. Essays*, iii. pp. 109, 185.   [2] *Ib.*, iii. p. 410.
[3] *Ib.*, ix. pp. 223-225.

complexity, and has, in future, to fit himself into that organisation, or be crushed by it, it is needful not only that boys
and girls should be made acquainted with the elementary
laws of conduct, but that their affections should be trained
so as to love with all their hearts that conduct which tends
to the attainment of the highest good for themselves and
their fellow-men, and to hate with all their hearts that
opposite course of action which is fraught with evil.[1]

Lacking this, intellectual training may be as productive
of harm as of good ; reading, writing, and ciphering may
equip a youth for forgery, and training in mechanics make
him an expert burglar.   In the year before his election
on the School Board, Huxley thus summed up what in
his judgement is comprised in a liberal education :—

That man, I think, has had a liberal education who has
been so trained in youth that his body is the ready servant of
his will, and does with ease and pleasure all the work that,
as a mechanism, it is capable of ; whose intellect is a clear,
cold logic-engine, with all its parts of equal strength and in
smooth working order ; ready, like a steam-engine, to be
turned to any kind of work, and spin the gossamers as well
as forge the anchors of the mind ; whose mind is stored
with the knowledge of the great and fundamental truths of
nature and of the laws of her operations ; one who, no
stunted ascetic, is full of fire and life, but whose passions are
trained to come to heel by a vigorous will, the servant
of a tender conscience ; who has learned to love all beauty,
whether of nature or of art, to hate all vileness, and to
respect others as himself.   Such an one, and no other, I
conceive, has had a liberal education ; for he is, as completely as a man can be, in harmony with Nature.   He will
make the best of her, and she of him.   They will get on

---

[1] *Coll. Essays,* iii. p. 393.

together rarely : she as his ever beneficent mother ; he as her mouthpiece, her conscious self, her minister and interpreter.[1]

In moral training, or the application of knowledge to conduct, Huxley would accord no place to theology. If the various denominations, whether Church or Dissenting, choose to start and maintain schools in which their several tenets are to be taught, that is their affair. They pay the piper, and they may call the tune. But schools established and maintained by the community depart from their proper functions when they train "either hands for factories or congregations for churches."[2] They are to hold no brief for any sect. The ethics which they teach must have relation to life, and therefore must be neither technical nor speculative. Theology is both, and cannot be otherwise. Moreover, where order is present, it imports confusion ; it, and it alone, is the apple of discord, and its dogmas, on many of which no two sects are agreed, bring "not peace, but a sword." The teaching of the ascertained facts of history, astronomy, geology, and other branches of science ; the inculcation of the duties of cleanliness and temperance ; of self-respect and self-restraint ; of consideration for others ; of kindness to animals ; and of honesty and truthfulness in all the relations of life—all which, enforced by example and illustration, can be brightly conveyed,—these run smoothly enough and arouse no bitterness. It is over the disputable creed and

[1] *Lay Sermons*, p. 30.   [2] I. 351.

dogma; over the unproven—nay, as the well-informed among clergy and laity know, the disproved—that the precious time of youthhood is wasted, and the battle for capture of the schools is waged. "By their fruits ye shall know them." And if the moral tone of the generation which has been brought up on the creeds and the catechism satisfies the teachers as to the practical influence of these on the lives of the taught, it is clear that a low standard contents them.

Knowing Huxley's antagonistic attitude towards orthodox beliefs, both cleric and secularist were bewildered when the "great Agnostic," as the *Spectator* called him, pronounced himself in favour of the use of the Bible in Board Schools. That his decision was ruled by the highest motives *va sans dire*, but, as he came to see, it was none the less deplorable. On the eve of the election he explained his position as follows :—

When the great mass of the English people declare that they want to have the children in the elementary schools taught the Bible, and when it was plain from the terms of the Act that it was intended that such Bible-reading should be permitted, unless good cause for prohibiting it could be shown, I do not see what reason there is for opposing that wish. Certainly, I, individually, could with no shadow of consistency oppose the teaching of the children of other people that which my own children are taught to do. And even if the reading of the Bible were not, as I think it is, consonant with political reason and justice, and with a desire to act in the spirit of the education measure, I am disposed to think it might still be well to read that book in the elementary schools.

I have always been strongly in favour of secular education, in the sense of education without theology ; but I must confess I have been no less seriously perplexed to know by what practical measures the religious feeling, which is the essential basis of conduct, was to be kept up, in the present utterly chaotic state of opinion, without the use of the Bible. The Pagan moralists lack life and colour, and even the noble Stoic, Marcus Aurelius, is too high and refined for an ordinary child. Take the Bible as a whole : make the severest deductions which fair criticism can dictate for shortcomings and positive errors; eliminate, as a sensible lay-teacher would do, if left to himself, all that it is not desirable for children to occupy themselves with ; and there still remains in this old literature a vast residuum of moral beauty and grandeur. And then consider the great historical fact that, for three centuries, this book has been woven into the life of all that is best and noblest in English history ; that it has become the national epic of Britain, and is as familiar to noble and simple, from John-o'-Groat's House to Land's End, as Dante and Tasso once were to the Italians ; that it is written in the noblest and purest English, and abounds in exquisite beauties of mere literary form ; and, finally, that it forbids the veriest hind who never left his village to be ignorant of the existence of other countries and other civilisations, and of a great past, stretching back to the furthest limits of the oldest nations in the world. By the study of what other book could children be so much humanised and made to feel that each figure in that vast historical procession fills, like themselves, but a momentary space in the interval between two eternities ; and earns the blessings or the curses of all time, according to its effort to do good and hate evil, even as they also are earning their payment for their work ?

On the whole, then, I am in favour of reading the Bible, with such grammatical, geographical, and historical explanations by a lay-teacher as may be needful, with rigid exclusion of any further theological teaching than that contained in the Bible itself. And in stating what this is, the teacher would do well not to go beyond the precise words of the Bible ; for if he does, he will, in the first place, undertake a task beyond his strength, seeing that all the Jewish and Christian sects have been at work upon that subject for more than two thousand years, and have not yet arrived, and are not in the least likely to arrive, at an agreement ; and, in the second place, he will certainly begin to teach something distinctively denominational, and thereby come into violent collision with the Act of Parliament.[1]

As is well known, the so - called Cowper - Temple clause in the Act, which is itself an unsatisfactory compromise, prescribes that " no religious catechism or religious formulary which is distinctive of any particular denomination shall be taught in the school "; and Huxley believed that, in the words of W. E. Forster, no attempt would be made to cram into the children's " poor little minds theological dogmas which their tender age prevents them from understanding." [2]   He mistrusted the clergy ; but he had faith that, in lay hands, " the teaching of that ' venerable record of ancient life, miscalled a book,' [3] would be gradually modified into harmony with common-sense." But in his belief that his opponents would abide by the compact, he assumed that their standard of honour and integrity was not lower than his own. He was mistaken. The bargain has not been kept by the clerical party, and attempt after attempt has been, and is being, made to reduce the Cowper-Temple clause to a nullity. Theological

[1] *Coll. Essays*, iii. pp. 397-399.

[2] I. 344.

[3] II. 123.

bias, or fear of retarded promotion, have made many of
the teachers puppets in the hands of the parsons.   The
Bible is not interpreted, as Jowett said it should be,
"like any other book," and this to the grievous impair-
ment of its value, since appreciation of it is deepened in
the degree that it is freed from the shackles of theories
of inspiration.   Its miscellaneous contents, many of them
of uncertain authorship and of disputed meaning, are
presented as constituting one harmonious supernatural
document ; its myths are still taught as history ; and the
Ten Commandments are put on the same high ethical
plane as the Beatitudes.

Not very long before his death Huxley was asked to
take part in opposing the tactics known as " Rileyism."
To this he replied :—

I feel very strongly about the attempt to capture
elementary education on the part of the orthodox sects,
in spite of the clear pledges given by Forster, and the
understanding arrived at by the first School Board.   Unfortunately, I am entangled in several undertakings, which
I did not bargain for, and could not refuse, and which will
occupy all my scanty working powers for some months to
come.   So I must really keep out of the *melée*.   Indeed, I
am not sure but that the best policy is to let these Christian
pagans have their way.   The axe is laid to the root of
the tree, and when it falls they will be crushed the more
effectually for their short success.[1]

---

[1] *Westminster Gazette*, 1st July 1895 ; and see I. 343 (note).   In
his *Bible in School*, p. 12, Mr Allanson Picton says that shortly
before his death Huxley expressed regret that he had not voted with
Mr Picton for the exclusion of the Bible from elementary schools.

While " ecclesiastically-minded persons," not content with absorbing one entire day in the week, and some portion of other days, clamoured for more, Huxley retorted by asking them to surrender a portion of the Sunday

for the purpose of instructing those who have no other leisure in a knowledge of the phenomena of Nature, and of man's relation to Nature. I should like to see a scientific Sunday-school in every parish, not for the purpose of superseding any existing means of teaching the people the things that are for their good, but side by side with them. I cannot but think that there is room for all of us to work in helping to bridge over the great abyss of ignorance which lies at our feet.[1]

As late as 1893 he planned-out a series of working men's lectures on the Bible, " in which he should present to the unlearned the results of scientific study of the documents, and do for theology what he had done for zoology thirty years before "; and although this scheme, the outline of which Mr Leonard Huxley copies from his father's notebook, was never carried out, " it was constantly before Huxley's mind during the two years left to him." [2] Before leaving the subject of his general influence as an educational reformer, it should be noted that he worked with an apostolic fervour to improve the quality of the teachers as the only security for thorough education of the taught. He established regular classes for the training of " scientific mission-aries," [3] as he described them ; pressed his views on

[1] *Lay Sermons*, p. 61.   [2] II. 345.   [3] I. 377.

technical education on the City guilds and other influential bodies, and kept before his students, as the mark
of their "high calling,"

the cultivation of that enthusiasm for truth, that fanaticism
of veracity which is a greater possession than much learning,
a nobler gift than the power of increasing knowledge; by so
much greater than these as the moral nature of man is
greater than the intellectual.[1]

Owing to a serious breakdown in health, Huxley was
compelled, after fourteen months' service on the School
Board, to resign his membership. "A wealthy friend
wrote to him in the most honourable and delicate terms,
begging him, on public grounds, to accept £400 a-year
to enable him to continue his work on the Board. He
refused the offer as simply and straightforwardly as it
was made; his means, though not large, were sufficient
for his present needs."[2] Some, who had no personal
knowledge of him, thought that his desire to secure a
seat on the School Board indicated an intention to enter
Parliament. But he had neither taste nor ambition for
politics.

At a Royal Society dinner in 1892, Mr Shaw Lefevre
expressed his regret that Huxley's abilities had never
been placed at the service of the House of Commons.
In his reply, reminiscences of youth and of controversies
in recent years found a place. He told the company
that, when he was a very young man, a lawyer in good
practice, believing that he saw in him qualities that

[1] *Coll. Essays*, iii. p. 205.   [2] I. 353.

would ensure success at the bar, offered to advance him an income for a certain number of years until he could repay the amount from the fees which he was sure to earn. He declined, because, as he dryly said,

so far as I understand myself, my faculties are so entirely confined to the discovery of truth, that I have no sort of power of obscuring it.

In 1870, Huxley's defence of Dr Brown-Séquard at the Liverpool meeting of the British Association brought him into collision with the opponents of vivisection, and the battle went on, in intermittent fashion, for some seven years. Experiments had been carried on, chiefly in France, without regard to animal suffering, and also for the wholly needless purpose of further demonstrating well-known facts in physiology and pathology. Hence an agitation which, within limits, commanded the sympathy of all humanely minded folk, and the appointment of a committee by the Association to consider what steps should be taken to reduce to its minimum the suffering entailed by legitimate inquiry. The committee recommended that there should be no experiments without the use of anæsthetics; or for the purpose of illustrating truths already known; or for practice in manual dexterity; and these provisions, with others of undue stringency, were embodied in "An Act to amend the law relating to Cruelty to Animals," passed in 1876. Huxley held that "the wanton infliction of pain on man or beast is a crime," [1] and that the vivisectionist is justi-

[1] I. 436.

fied only when his aim is the discovery of the origin
and nature of disease with a view to the alleviation or
removal of the suffering which it causes. In this he
has rendered incalculable service to mankind, and also
to the lower animals, since "not a single one of all the
great truths of modern physiology has been established
otherwise than by experiments on living things."[1]

In defending a practice which by one successful
experiment on an animal rendered insensible to pain
might save numberless lives from some fell disease,
Huxley had to meet a frontal attack, whose chief
weapon, wielded by fanaticism, was misrepresentation
and slander. He was charged by one of the so-called
"religious" papers with advocating the practice of vivisection before children, and the charge was repeated in
the House of Lords. It was necessary to publicly deny
what had been thus publicly asserted ; he quoted chapter
and verse from his *Elementary Physiology* in refutation,
adding that "personally and constitutionally" the per-
formance of experiments upon living and conscious
animals was "so extremely disagreeable" to himself
that he had "never followed any line of investigation
in which such experiments were required." But he said
that, as a teacher of physiology, he could not

consent to be prohibited from showing the circulation in a
frog's foot, because the frog is made slightly uncomfortable
by being tied up for that purpose ; nor from showing the
fundamental properties of nerves, because extirpating the

---

[1] I. 434.

brain of the same animal inflicts one - thousandth part of
the prolonged suffering which it undergoes when it makes
its natural exit from the world by being slowly forced down
the throat of a duck, and crushed and asphyxiated in that
creature's stomach.[1]

He had small stock of patience for the "sentimental
hypocrisy" which evidenced its lack of sincerity in not
abstaining from eating the flesh of creatures put to death
in lingering torture, both in the slaughter-house and on
the moors, or in destroying rats, mice, and other "sen-
tient vermin"; and when the Act of 1876, on the Royal
Commission concerning which he was a member, was
passed, he showed how it exemplified the old adage
that "one man may steal a horse while the other may
not look over the hedge."

While, as a member of a late Royal Commission, I did
my best to prevent the infliction of needless pain for any
purpose, I think it is my duty to take this opportunity of
expressing my regret at a condition of the law which permits
a boy to troll for pike or set lines with live-frog bait for idle
amusement, and at the same time lays the teacher of that
boy open to the penalty of fine and imprisonment if he uses
the same animal for the purpose of exhibiting one of the
most beautiful and instructive of physiological spectacles—
the circulation in the web of the foot.

So it comes about that in this year of grace 1877, two
persons may be charged with cruelty to animals. One has
impaled a frog, and suffered the creature to writhe about in
that condition for hours; the other has pained the animal no
more than one of us would be pained by tying strings round
his fingers and keeping him in the position of a hydropathic

---

[1] I. 432.

patient. The first offender says, " I did it because I find
fishing very amusing"; and the magistrate bids him depart
in peace, nay, probably wishes him good sport. The second
pleads, " I wanted to impress a scientific truth with a dis-
tinctness attainable in no other way on the minds of my
scholars," and the magistrate fines him five pounds.[1]

From 1870 onward, the time which Huxley had been
able to snatch from public and private demands for
biological research grew less and less. " For eight
years he was continuously on one Royal Commission
after another. His administrative work on learned
societies continued to increase ; in 1869-70 he held
the presidency of the Ethnological Society (which,
chiefly by his efforts, became merged in the Anthropological Institute); he was elected president of the
Geological Society in 1872 ; and for nearly ten years,
from 1871 to 1880, he was Secretary of the Royal
Society, an office which occupied no small portion of
his time and thought." [2] Little wonder, therefore, that
his dyspepsia became chronic, compelling a lengthy
absence, which, through the generosity of friends, was
spent along the Mediterranean seaboard as far as Egypt.[3]
Returning thence bronzed and bearded, but only patched
up, he perforce took life a little easier. In 1874 he
followed-up Tyndall's famous Presidential Address at
the Belfast meeting of the British Association with a
lecture on " Animal Automatism," which underwent
the usual misinterpretation attending any presentment

[1] *Coll. Essays*, iii. pp. 301-302.   [2] I. 324.   [3] I. 367.

of psychical activity in mechanical terms. In 1870, when lecturing before the Cambridge Young Men's Christian Society, Huxley had made the life and philosophy of Descartes the text of insistence on the duty of doubt as a condition of reaching certainty; and now, before a presumably more scientific audience, he showed what significant contributions that master-mind had made to our knowledge of the physiology of the nervous system. The resulting intrusion of the biologist into the domain of metaphysics, which theology had so long annexed, aroused the old antagonism, and Huxley had again to combat the passion and prejudice which his famous "lay sermon," on "The Physical Basis of Life," had aroused in Edinburgh in 1868.

The summer of 1875 found him in that city lecturing on Natural History on behalf of Sir (then Professor) Wyville Thomson, who was absent on the Challenger expedition. In a letter which Huxley received from Thomson in August, doubts were thrown on Huxley's theory of the organic character of a viscid, granular substance which had been dredged from the bottom of the Atlantic in 1868. He had expressed the opinion that this deposit was a living form of very low type, and in this faith, and as a compliment to Haeckel, had named it *Bathybius Haeckelii*.[1] But it turned out that what seemed to belong to the group of simplest living things was only a precipitate, probably due to its having been preserved in spirit.[2] There was an impression, confined, however,

[1] *Scientific Memoirs*, iii. p. 337.   [2] I. 295, 446; II. 5, 160.

to superficial critics, that Huxley had regarded Bathybius as a hitherto missing link between the living and
the not-living, and they rejoiced doubly; first, in his
discomfiture as possibly weakening his authority, and
next, in the blow dealt, as they hoped, to the theory
of the unity of the cosmos. But, as he told them, when
admitting the error,

> that which interested me in the matter was the apparent
> analogy of Bathybius with other well-known forms of lower
> life. . . . Speculative hopes and fears had nothing to
> do with the matter; and if Bathybius were brought up alive
> from the bottom of the Atlantic to-morrow, the fact would
> not have the slightest bearing, that I can discern, upon Mr
> Darwin's speculations, or upon any of the disputed problems
> of biology. It would merely be one elementary organism
> the more added to the thousands already known.[1]

Misrepresentation, whose roots were in animus rather
than in ignorance, went on, and as late as 1890 Mr
Mallock revived the " Bathybius myth " in the *Nineteenth Century*, upon which Huxley commented, with
warrantable irritation :—

> Bathybius is far too convenient a stick to beat this dog
> with to be ever given up, however many lies may be need-
> ful to make the weapon effectual. I told the whole story in
> my reply to the Duke of Argyll, but of course the pack give
> tongue just as loudly as ever. Clerically-minded people
> cannot be accurate, even the liberals.[2]

In 1876 he paid a long-cherished visit to America.
The newspapers, confusing him with Tyndall, recently

---

[1] *Coll. Essays*, v. p. 154.   [2] II. 160.

married to a daughter of the aristocratic house of Hamilton, reported that he was bringing with him his "titled bride," who, needless to say, had long been the joyful mother of many children. The trip interested and invigorated him; his progress from place to place was almost royal. But that with which his hosts thought to impress him most impressed him least. Their energy won his admiration; watching the mass of moving craft in New York harbour, he said, "If I were not a man, I think I should like to be a tug." But, in his lecture before the John Hopkins University at Baltimore, he said:—

I am not in the slightest degree impressed by your big-ness or your material resources, as such. Size is not grandeur; territory does not make a nation. The great issue, about which hangs a true sublimity, and the terror of overhanging fate, is—"What are you going to do with all these things?" . . . The one condition of success, your sole safeguard, is the moral worth and intellectual clear-ness of the individual citizen.

He was deeply interested in the fossil remains in the Yale College museum which Professor Marsh had un-earthed from the Tertiary beds of the Far West. They demonstrated what was new to him—the evolution of the horse on the American continent, "and for the first time indicated the direct line of descent of an existing animal." The fascinating story of the series of discov-eries, linking the one-toed genus Equus of to-day with a five-toed ancestor common to it and other hoofed quadrupeds, is told, with the added charm which

Huxley's power of clear exposition imparts, in his *American Addresses*. The subject will have fuller treatment in the next chapter.

In the following six years Huxley published as many books, among which, and of enduring value, were his monographs on the anatomy and physiology of the *Crayfish* and on the philosophy of *Hume*,—subjects seemingly diverse enough, but alike in the problems which they suggest concerning Nature as "nowhere inaccessible, and everywhere unfathomable."[1] In 1881, concurrently with the absorption of the School of Mines in what was then called the Normal School, Huxley became Professor of Biology and Dean of the Royal College of Science, claiming thereby, as he jocosely reminded his friends, the title of "The Very Reverend"; and in the same year he accepted an Inspectorship of Fisheries, which had the advantage of taking him into the fresh air.

In 1883 he received the highest honour which his fellow-savants could bestow in being elected President of the Royal Society. But the dignity, which he accepted with reluctance, was, on account of bad health, surrendered in November 1885. He had become more and more the invalid; holidays had given him only fillips, and the little store of energy which they added was quickly dissipated; deafness troubled him, bringing its dreaded isolation, and in the previous May, having reached his sixtieth year, an age at which he had often jocosely said that men of science should be pole-axed,

[1] *The Crayfish*, p. 3.

lest through ossification of mind they become arrestors of progress, he resigned all his appointments, paid and unpaid, and retired upon a pension of £1200 a-year, which, shortly afterwards, was supplemented by a Civil List pension of £300 a-year.

But resignation of offices meant not retirement from work. During the ten years of life that remained to him he was more in evidence than ever. He had never permitted his official position to curb his freedom of speech, and now that his time was all his own, that freedom could have larger play. In a retrospect of life, summing-up the part he had played in what he called the "New Reformation," he said that the objects which he had pursued were "briefly these":—

To promote the increase of natural knowledge and to forward the application of scientific methods of investigation to all the problems of life to the best of my ability, in the conviction which has grown with my growth and strengthened with my strength, that there is no alleviation for the sufferings of mankind except veracity of thought and of action, and the resolute facing of the world as it is, when the garment of make-belief by which pious hands have hidden its uglier features is stripped off. It is with this intent that I have subordinated any reasonable or unreasonable ambition for scientific fame which I may have permitted myself to entertain to other ends : to the popularisation of science ; to the development and organisation of scientific education ; to the endless series of battles and skirmishes over evolution ; and to untiring opposition to that ecclesiastical spirit, that clericalism which in England, and everywhere else, and to whatever denomination it may belong, is the deadly enemy of science.[1]

[1] *Coll. Essays*, i. p. 17.

The "battles and skirmishes over evolution" were now resolved by Huxley into a well-conceived plan of campaign in which all the forces that come of the widest knowledge and most varied experience were to be used in applying the doctrine of evolution to the demolition of beliefs which, in the degree that they are untrue, must be mischievous. But he was not merely critical and destructive : he razed only that he or others might raise. In the Prologue to his *Essays on Controverted Questions* he says that—

The present incarnation of the spirit of the Renascence differs from its predecessor in the eighteenth century, in that it builds up, as well as pulls down. That of which it has laid the foundation, of which it is already raising the superstructure, is the doctrine of Evolution, . . . a doctrine which is no speculation, but a generalisation of certain facts which may be observed by any one who will take the necessary trouble." [1]

Hence the inclusion therein of all that is of deepest import to man. Hence the inevitable, however tardy, supersession of theology as a body of speculative dogma by a religion having correspondence with the constitution and needs of human nature ; and the gradual displacement of ethics resting on ancient and shifting codes and conventions by ethics founded on what, after ages of sore testing, man has proven to be best for the welfare of society, and, therefore, as a social being, for himself.

Huxley's health, however, remained so indifferent

[1] *Coll. Essays,* v. pp. 41, 42.

that he needed stimulus to work. It came in unusual form from an article in the *Nineteenth Century* of November 1885, in which Mr Gladstone made a review of Dr Reville's *Prolegomena to the History of Religions* the vehicle of obsolete arguments in support of harmony between the Mosaic cosmogony and the theory of organic evolution. Re-stated by a man whose high authority in matters political had led many (for the logical faculty is, as yet, in the embryonic stage in the majority of minds) to accept him as an authority upon everything else, these arguments, refuted, as they had been, over and over again, had to be dealt with once more.[1] Huxley was the man for the task. The article, " he used humorously to say, so stirred his bile as to set his liver right at once ; " indeed, stagnation making him " unendurable to himself and everybody else," he said that he was thankful to " Providence " for specially devolving on Gladstone, Gore, & Co. the function of keeping " ''ome 'appy' for him."[2]

The controversies thus involved, together with essays on philosophical and social questions, filled the time between long intervals of broken health, and of sojourns on Alpine summits. Arolla made him feel young again :

> " Balm floating on thy mountain air
>   And healing sights to see ; "

but, eager to return to active life, he was " glad to see one's own dear native mud again. There is no foreign mud to come near it."[3] London, however, with its

[1] II. 425.   [2] II. 269.   [3] II. 103.

social beguilements, had long ceased to attract him, and the old home in Marlborough Place (charged for many a guest with delightful memories of Sunday evenings, with their conversation grave and gay), where he had lived since 1872, was given up, and Eastbourne fixed upon. There, through a timely legacy, he was able to build himself a house which he called Hodeslea, the ancestral form of the family name. There he lived from 1890 until his death, dividing his time between his books, his garden, and his grandchildren. He left it only at short and rare intervals to discharge the remnants of duties devolving upon him as honorary Dean of the Royal College of Science and as a Trustee of the British Museum. One notable journey was made in 1892. Fifteen years before then, Lord Salisbury had invited Huxley's opinion as to a "formal recognition of distinguished services in science, literature, and art by the granting of titles." Against this Huxley expressed himself strongly.[1] But when the dignity of a Privy Councillorship was offered him, he accepted it, because, as he wrote to Sir J. Donnelly—

I have always been dead against orders of merit and the like, but I think that men of letters and science who have been of use to the nation (Lord knows if I have) may fairly be ranked among its nominal or actual councillors.[2]

So, in August 1892, he went to kiss hands at Osborne, remembering, as he passed the old Victory, "that six-and-forty years ago he went up her side to report him-

[1] I. 359.　　　　　　　　[2] II. 323.

self on appointment as a poor devil of an assistant-surgeon." In the following October he was present at Tennyson's funeral, and but for a biting wind, would have been at Owen's in the following December. His "opinion of the man's character" never altered; but death "ends all quarrels," and at the request of Owen's grandson and biographer he contributed a chapter on "Owen's Place in Anatomical Science," which enabled him to pay honest tribute to the value and importance of Owen's work in that branch of biology. Friends were falling out of the ranks: in the autumn of 1893 Jowett, Tyndall, and Sir Andrew Clark passed away, bringing home the thought that "one should always be ready to stand at attention when the order to march comes." [1]

Oxford had seen little of Huxley since the day of his famous duel with its bishop in 1860. Ten years later, Pusey and his party had prevented the conferring of the degree of D.C.L. on Owen—although he was *persona grata* to the Episcopal bench—as well as on Froude and Huxley. But, tardily following the sister and other universities, Oxford reversed the decision in 1885. Eight years later, Huxley revisited the "home of lost causes" to deliver the Romanes Lecture on *Evolution and Ethics*. The occasion may rank as historic.

The Sheldonian Theatre was thronged before he appeared upon the platform, a striking presence in his D.C.L. robes,

[1] II. 368.

and looking very leonine with his long silvery grey hair
sweeping back in one long wave from his forehead, and the
rugged squareness of his features tempered by the benignity
of an old age which has seen much and overcome much.
He read the lecture from a printed copy, not venturing, as he
would have liked, upon the severe task of speaking it from
memory, considering its length and the importance of
preserving the exact wording.[1]

In August 1894 the temptation offered by the meeting
of the British Association at Oxford to renew a visit was
too strong to be resisted, if only for the contrast of feelings which the occasion would awaken. Huxley might
aptly have applied to himself the ancient words with
which he ended his lecture *On the Coming of Age of
the Origin of Species:* "The stone which the builders
rejected the same is become the head of the corner."
Lord Salisbury was president, and in his address, while
admitting that Darwin had, "as a matter of fact, disposed
of the doctrine of the immutability of species," he raised
a number of disingenuous objections to the general theory
of what he ironically called the "comforting word, Evolution," objections evidencing the "biassed amateur" and
the "representative of ecclesiastical conservatism and
orthodoxy." Huxley had consented to second the vote
of thanks to the president, and although "the old Adam,
of course, prompted the tearing of the address to pieces,
which would have been a very easy job," he had perforce to content himself with "conveying criticism in
the shape of praise."[2] However, he dealt with the

[1] II. 356.   [2] II. 379.

"polemical dexterity" of the Marquis and gave him
"a Roland for his Oliver" in an article on "Past and
Present" in *Nature*, 1st November 1894. In that
month the Royal Society put its final seal to Huxley's
life-work in awarding him the Darwin medal; and in his
speech at the anniversary dinner acknowledging the
compliment, a speech whose impressiveness can never
fade from the memory of those who heard it, he also
set the "seal to his ministry" in emphasising his belief

that the views which were propounded by Mr Darwin thirty-
five years ago may be understood hereafter as constituting
an epoch in the intellectual history of the human race. They
will modify the whole system of our thought and opinion,
our most intimate convictions.

With the exception of a hurried visit to London in
January 1895 to join as spokesman in a deputation to
Lord Salisbury on a cause near his heart, that of London University Reform, he never left Eastbourne again.
The last thing which he wrote was a criticism of Mr
Balfour's "quaintly-entitled" (the happy phrase is Mr
Leslie Stephen's) *Foundations of Belief*.[1] He had to
deal with the same vagueness, elusiveness, and want
of insight into the position travestied which is the
feature of Mr Gladstone's polemics, and which make
Mr Balfour, trained as he is in the same atmosphere
of obscuration of the truth and of dialectical fencing,
the intellectual representative of that master of the art
of mystification. In returning the proofs of the first

[1] See *infra*, p. 204.

part of the article to the editor of the *Nineteenth
Century*, Huxley wrote :—

> My estimation of Balfour, as a thinker, sinks lower and
> lower the farther I go. God help the people who think his
> book an important contribution to thought ! The Giga-
> dibsians [1] who say so are past divine assistance.[2] . . . A. B.
> is the incarnation of Gigadibs. I should call him *Giga-
> dibsius Optimus Maximus*.[3]

The second part was never published ; its incompletion
has curious parallel in the following extract from a
letter written by Huxley to Tyndall in 1854 :—

> The poor fellow vanished in the middle of an unfinished
> article, which has appeared in the last *Westminster*, as his
> forlorn Vale ! to the world. After all, that is the way to die,
> —better a thousand times than drivelling off into eternity
> betwixt awake and asleep in a fatuous old age.[4]

From March onwards old complications were aggravated
by influenza, and although he threw this off, it left him
weaker for the struggle, yet hopeful of the issue. On
the 26th June he wrote in cheerful tone to his old
friend Hooker ; but on the afternoon of the 29th he
passed away, "the Fates," as he had prayed, leaving
him "clear and vigorous mind "[5] to the end.

It has become a fashion to more or less burden a

---

[1] " You Gigadibs who, thirty years of age,
    Believe you see two points in Hamlet's soul
    Unseized by the Germans yet—which view you'll print."
        —*Bishop Blougram's Apology*—BROWNING.
        (Quoted by Huxley, *Nineteenth Century*,
        March 1895, p. 528.

[2] II. 400.   [3] II. 430.   [4] I. 121.   [5] II. 361.

man's biography with tributes to his worth from his friends. Such "appreciations," as these witnesses to character are called, weaken rather than strengthen, since their presence implies their possible necessity. Of these credentials Huxley stands in no need. He is his own witness in the work which he did, and in the spirit which informed it. Those who knew him best loved him most, and none came into touch with his eager, sympathetic, breezy, and altogether beautiful nature without receiving an impulse to higher aims. Of spotless integrity in every relation, and single-minded in every purpose, he went on from strength to strength, because each step made the rightness of the path which he had chosen more manifest. One "who never turned his back, but marched breast forward"; unswayed by motives of worldly prudence; undeterred by authority which could produce no valid warrant of its claims; governed by "morality touched by emotion," and guided by reason within limits which none have defined so well,—he remains alike an example and an inspiration to all men for all time.

II.

THE DISCOVERER.

In the preface to the eighth volume of his *Collected Essays* Huxley says :—

It must be admitted that the popularisation of science, whether by lectures or by essays, has its drawbacks. Success in this department has its perils for those who succeed. The "people who fail" take their revenge by ignoring all the rest of a man's work, and glibly labelling him a mere populariser. If the falsehood were not too glaring, they would say the same of Faraday, and Helmholtz, and Kelvin.[1]

They said it of Huxley. In a recent compilation entitled *One Hundred and One Great Writers*, issued under the editorship of so well-equipped a scholar as Dr Richard Garnett, Huxley's work is described as "that of the populariser; the man who makes few original contributions to science or thought, but states the discoveries of others better than they could have stated them themselves." And, doubtless, that is a very common impression about a man the titles of

[1] P. vii.

whose original scientific papers [1] fill ten pages of the
appendix to his biography.[2] The fact is, he loomed so
large in the public eye as the most luminous expositor
of the theory of organic evolution, as the proclaimer of
its significance, and as the protagonist in the great
revolution which it has brought about, that the importance of his discoveries in biology is obscured. And
there is further explanation, which is given by Mr
Chalmers Mitchell in his admirable monograph, *Thomas
Henry Huxley : a Sketch of his Life and Work.* He
says :—

The years that have passed since 1850 have seen not only
the most amazing progress in our knowledge of comparative
anatomy, but almost a revolution in the methods of studying
it. Huxley's work has been incorporated in the very body
of science. A large number of later investigators have
advanced upon the lines he laid down ; and just as the
superstructures of a great building conceal the foundations,
so later anatomical work, although it has only amplified and
extended Huxley's discoveries, has made them seem less
striking to the modern reader. The present writer, for
instance, learned all that he knows of anatomy in the last
ten years, and until he turned to it for the purpose of this
volume he had never referred to Huxley's original paper.
[Mr Chalmers Mitchell is here speaking of the Memoir on
the Medusæ.] When he did so, he found from beginning to
end nothing that was new to him, nothing that was strange ;
all the ideas in the memoir had passed into the currency of
knowledge, and he had been taught them as fundamental
facts. It was only when he turned to the text-books of

---

[1] Now collected in four volumes under the editorship of Sir
Michael Foster and Professor E. Ray Lankester.

[2] II. 460-470.

anatomy and natural history current in Huxley's time that he was able to realise how the conclusions of the young ship-surgeon struck the President and Fellows of the Royal Society as luminous and revolutionary ideas.[1]

And again :—

Huxley's work upon birds, like his work in many other branches of anatomy, has been so overlaid by the investigations of subsequent zoologists that it is easy to overlook its importance. His employment of the skeleton as the basis of classification was succeeded by the work of others who made a similar use of the muscular anatomy, of the intestinal canal, of the windpipe, of the tendons of the feet, and many other structures which display anatomical modifications in different birds. . . . Huxley's anatomical work was essentially living and stimulating, and too often it has become lost to sight simply because of the vast superstructures of new facts to which it gave rise.[2]

The centring of Huxley's interest in the apparatus and functions of living things has been named, as also the opportunity for exercise of this which his voyage in the Rattlesnake supplied. The dredge brought him strange dwellers of the deep sea — fantastic in form, delicate in structure, and exquisite in colour. These he sketched with his facile pencil, dissected, and, whenever chance offered, compared, giving special attention to the family of the Medusæ, his memoir on which laid the foundation-stone of his scientific fame. It should be noted that that memoir was written in 1848, eleven

[1] Pp. 34, 35.
[2] *Ib.*, p. 137. The third, fifth, and eighth chapters of Mr Chalmers Mitchell's book are to be strongly commended for the clear and accurate account of Huxley's original work which they furnish.

years before the publication of the *Origin of Species*, because in determining the value of any scientific, and, especially, of biological work, its chronological place must be taken into account.   In science the Old and the New Dispensation may be severally defined as the Pre-Darwinian and the Post-Darwinian, and perhaps a brief survey of what advance towards knowledge of the fundamental unity of living things had been reached during the Old Dispensation may make clearer the bearing of Huxley's discoveries, and explain why their significance was not apparent even to himself.

The great name of Aristotle is associated with the earliest attempt at a classification of animals.   This was based, in the main, on likenesses of external structure, and was accepted, without fundamental variation, for the long period of eighteen hundred years.   The first step towards any important revision was taken, in the seventeenth century, by Ray, "the father of modern zoology."   In the eighteenth century Boerhaave's experiments proved that all living things are built up of the same materials, while Hunter demonstrated the likenesses in animal structure.   Towards the close of that century, Linnæus had completed his great scheme of classification of plants and animals, dividing the latter into six classes : the Vertebrates into *mammals*, *birds*, *amphibians* (including reptiles), and *fishes ;* and the Invertebrates into *insects* and *worms*.   Aristotle had conceived of life as a ladder whose steps represented the several animals in ascending scale : Lamarck (to whom Huxley pays high tribute [1]), with genuine insight, depicted it as a many-branched tree, and therefore, as interrelated and interdependent. Cuvier reduced Linnæus's six divisions to four : *Vertebrata*, or backboned (fishes to men) ; *Mollusca*, or soft-bodied (snails, oysters, &c.) ; *Articulata*, or jointed (spiders, bees, ants, &c.), and *Radiata*, or rayed (jelly-fish, polyps, sea-anemones).

Meanwhile, the microscope, by which, in the middle of the seventeenth century, Malpighi had made pioneer discoveries, was becoming more and more the important instrument of examination of the internal structure of living things, and hence opening the way to inquiry into their origin and history. The study of anatomy advanced to comparison of the structures and of the several corresponding organs in divers plants and animals, and of the functions discharged by those organs ; hence the rise of the comparative method, with its demonstration of fundamental relations between living things. Schleiden discovered that the cell is the unit of plant - life ; and Schwann proved that the same is true of animals. Harvey's formula of development, " All life comes from an egg " (*omne vivum ex ovo*), gave place to the doctrine of *omnis cellula e cellula*. The lowest animals are one-celled, or, sometimes, a loosely connected cluster of cells ; all other animals are built-up of a number of cells, whence tissues and organs are developed. In 1844, five years after Schwann's demonstration, Von Mohl showed that each cell contains a viscous, granular-look-

[1] II. 59.

ing, highly active substance, the result of a very complex union of carbon (to which Haeckel assigns the chief activity), hydrogen, oxygen, and nitrogen. This substance is known as protoplasm, and is, in Huxley's familiar phrase, "the physical basis of life." Some years before this, Von Baer had observed that the embryos of birds, dogs, fish, and other backboned animals, including man, are all alike during their earlier stages. It is concerning Von Baer's writings that Huxley said none had made so great an impression on him down to the publication of the *Origin of Species*[1]; and it was in Von Baer's *Law of Development* that Mr Spencer found hints and evidence supporting his own theory of advance from the simple to the complex as applied to the cosmos.

The effect of these discoveries was to produce an unsettled feeling as to the truth of the doctrine of the fixity of species. Lamarck was the most prominent, but not the only, naturalist of the eighteenth century to suggest that the various species had not been separately created, but had been developed by sundry causes, operating through long ages, from a few simple forms. It was a perilous step in those days of the long-reaching secular arm to throw doubt on the account of the creation contained in a document which God Himself was believed to have inspired; but the doubt once harboured, a mass of facts telling against the orthodox

[1] I. 175, and cf. 163.

view came into unwonted significance. Every scheme of classification hitherto propounded had assumed the immutability of the several groups; the conception of any fundamental relation of the several types to a common primitive type was unborn; and the most superficial comparison between the vertebrates, in which some structural resemblances were obvious, and the loose and confused medley covered by the term invertebrate, was sufficient to negative any idea of an underlying unity that might be broached.

The illustrious Cuvier regarded the several groups as the outcome of a preordained plan of the Creator, and believed that each successive annihilation of plants and animals was followed by a fresh creative fiat. His most distinguished pupil, Owen, likewise explained the succession of species as the operation of "a continuously creational law." But, nevertheless, facts were pouring in which could not be thus interpreted. The fossil-yielding rocks, whose contents both these great anatomists were arranging, making the dry bones tell the story of a long and connected life-history, and of the descent of certain existing animals along well-marked ancestral lines, were to prove the most sure foundation on which the doctrine of organic evolution rests. Lyell's *Principles of Geology* raised the question, "If natural causation is competent to account for the not-living part of the globe, why should it not account for the living part?" Herbert Spencer was asking

which was the more rational theory to account for the
existence of millions of species :—

Is it most likely that there have been ten millions of
special creations ; or is it most likely that by continual modifications, due to change of circumstances, ten millions of
varieties have been produced as varieties are being produced
still ?[1]

The answer to that question — an answer which
involved the putting of more momentous questions—
was not forthcoming for another seven years. As for
Huxley's position in the matter, he says, in the chapter
"On the Reception of the Origin of Species," which he
contributed to Darwin's *Life and Letters*, that he was
"not brought into serious contact with the 'species'
question until after 1850." He had "long done with
the Pentateuchal cosmogony," and he rejected all
theories of "archetypal ideas," "perfecting principles,"
and the like ; but the frequent discussions which he had
with Mr Spencer from 1852 onwards failed to drive
him from his "agnostic position." His difficulties were
twofold :—

Firstly, that up to that time the evidence in favour of
transmutation was wholly insufficient ; and secondly, that
no suggestion respecting the causes of transmutation
assumed, which had been made, was in any way adequate
to explain the phenomena. Looking back at the state of
knowledge at that time, I really do not see that any other
conclusion was justifiable.[2]

----

[1] *Leader*, 20th March 1852.
[2] Darwin's *Life and Letters*, ii. p. 188.

He sums up his attitude in two words, as that of "critical expectancy."

> "Wandering between two worlds : one dead,
> The other powerless to be born."

At his first interview with Darwin he expressed, "with all the confidence of youth and imperfect knowledge," his belief in the sharpness of the lines of demarcation between natural groups, and in the absence of transitional forms.

I was not aware, at that time, that he had been many years brooding over the species question ; and the humourous smile which accompanied his gentle answer, that such was not altogether his view, long haunted and puzzled me.[1]

The incident may have recalled to his mind an interview with Faraday in the old student days at Charing Cross Hospital, of which he tells in one of his letters from the Rattlesnake. He had made one of the manifold attempts to realise perpetual motion, and, having put his scheme on paper, took it to the Royal Institution, at the door of which he ran against "a little man in a brown coat." The "little man" was Faraday, who, although he knew nothing of Huxley, at once looked at the plan which he had drawn, and then asked him if he "was acquainted with mechanism, what we call the laws of motion ?"

I saw that all was up with my poor scheme, so after trying a little to explain, in the course of which I certainly failed in giving him a clear idea of what I would be at, I thanked him for his attention, and went off as dissatisfied as ever.[2]

---

[1] Darwin's *Life and Letters*, ii. p. 196.   [2] I. 22.

Needless to say, as with himself and Darwin, the two were to meet in very different relations in a few years, when Huxley's sense of humour would impel him to remind Faraday of the lesson learned from him.

The more important of Huxley's original contributions to biological science may now be set forth, with as much freedom from technical terms as the subjects permit.

The discoveries of Schleiden and Schwann in cell-structure, as well as those of Von Baer in comparative embryology, were known to Huxley when, "with micro-scope lashed to the mast," he examined the fragile organisms, "as the sand of the sea-shore innumerable." To those discoveries he made an important addition in detecting that the Medusæ are built up of two cell-layers, or "foundation-membranes," enclosing a stomach-cavity. From the outer layer the skin and nervous system (as to the existence of which latter, since proven, Huxley was at the time doubtful) are developed ; and from the inner layer the alimentary and other organs are developed. He also found that the reproductive organs are external, and that all the Medusæ have thread-cells wherewith poison is discharged at their prey. He then made search for the presence of these several features in other families of the Hydrozoa, and found unity of plan throughout. In modern classification, there are three grades of animals : the Protozoa, which embrace only the one-celled ; and the Cœlenterata and Cœlomata, grouped as many-celled, under the term Metazoa. Even this scheme is under modification—the animals known as sponges being now assigned a separate place as "an independent and sterile branch of the tree of life," a branch, perhaps, in direct descent from the one-celled organism.[1] The Medusæ, hydra, and sea-anemones are grouped under Cœlenterata, or hollow-bodied, comprising all two-layered animals. The Cœlomata comprise all animals in which a third foundation-membrane has been developed, and which possess a cœlom, or true stomach, with blood-vessels. They embrace every animal from a worm to a man.

Huxley's next step was to compare the two foundation-membranes of the Cœlenterata with the serous and mucous layers of the embryos of vertebrates ; and here, although he then guessed it not, he made a contribution of the highest importance to the doctrine of descent. Von Baer had shown the resemblances between all back-boned animals in their passage from the embryo to the adult state, and Huxley showed that, in still earlier stages of their development, they exhibited the two foundation-membranes of the Cœlenterata, thus recording, as it were, the history of their evolution from those lower organisms. It is easy enough to us, looking back, to see what a key to the proof of the fundamental unity of living things this supplied ; but even the prevision of Huxley, shown so markedly in many ways, was obscured by the domin-ance of the notion of fixity outside certain well-marked lines. For in 1853 he writes that "there is no pro-

[1] *A Treatise on Zoology.* Part II. The Porifera and Cœlenterata. Edited by E. Ray Lankester, F.R.S.

gression from a lower to a higher type, but merely a
more or less complete evolution of one type." Nevertheless, his acute comparison between the Cœlenterata
and the Cœlomata was destined to supply proof of the
progression which he questioned. His discovery, says
Professor Allman,

that the body of the Medusæ is essentially composed of two
membranes, an outer and an inner, and his recognition of
these as the homologues of the two primary germinal leaflets
in the vertebrate embryo, is one of the greatest claims of his
splendid work on the recognition of zoologists. This discovery stands at the very base of a philosophical zoology, and
of a true conception of the affinities of animals. It is the
ground on which Haeckel has founded his famous Gastræa-
theory, and without it Kowalesky could never have announced
his great discovery of the affinity of the Ascidians and Vertebrates, by which zoologists have been startled.[1]

Noting, by the way, that before Huxley sailed in the
Rattlesnake, he had made the interesting discovery that
the composition of the blood of the lancelet, a very low
vertebrate, approached that of the blood of the higher
vertebrates, we find his work on the Medusæ followed
by a further contribution to knowledge of organic relation in an examination of the structure of the sea-
squirts, or Ascidians, so called from their resemblance
to a double-necked bottle (Greek *askidion*, a small
bottle). These animals are found singly, and also
in clusters, and interest in them, as hinted in the quotation from Professor Allman, has deepened since the

[1] I. 40.

discovery that they are in the line of the development from invertebrate to vertebrate which ends in man himself. Still feeling his way towards the great central doctrine of unity, denial of which is the only heresy from which a man need pray to be delivered, Huxley made Schwann's cell-theory the basis of examination into the identity of structure in plants and animals. He showed—and this with luminous skill in the famous "lay sermon" on "The Physical Basis of Life"—that the cell is the unit of structure, and not the unit of function ; that, in technical terms, it is morphological, not physiological, the "protoplasm" being the fundamental element. "Although," remarks Professor Ray Lankester—

it is forty years since the "Review of the Cell Theory" was published, and although our knowledge of cell-structure has made immense progress during those forty years, yet the main contention of that article—viz., that cells are not the cause but the result of organisation, in fact are, as Huxley says, to the tide of life what the line of shells and weeds on the sea-shore is to the tide of the living sea—is even now being reasserted, and, in a slightly modified form, is by very many cytologists admitted as having more truth in it than the opposed view and its later outcomes, to the effect that the cell is the unit of life in which and through which alone living matter manifests our activities.[1]

The contents of the *Scientific Memoirs* show that in all the papers which Huxley contributed to the Royal Society and other learned bodies, his researches were

[1] I. 140.

ruled not so much by the desire to classify and label specimens as to establish affinities between organisms, and to supersede the ill-assorted jumble, which, for example, lumped crabs and bees together under one heading, by an orderly and demonstrable classification. Down to 1854, when he succeeded Forbes at the School of Mines, his studies had been restricted to invertebrates ; but from that period, fossil forms, for which, as already remarked, he had no taste,[1] were to occupy a main portion of his time. They appeared to take him off the main track that might lead to a great generalisation : he saw no solution of the problem of transmutation save in study of the living thing ; there was, as he said in a lecture at the Royal Institution in 1855, "no real parallel between the successive forms assumed in the development of the life of the individual at present, and those which have appeared at different epochs in the past." But, so complete was the revolution effected by the *Origin of Species*, that in 1878 he wrote :—

On the evidence of palæontology, the evolution of many existing forms of animal life from their predecessors is no longer an hypothesis but an historical fact.[2]

While, in an address to the British Association at York two years afterwards, he said :—

If the doctrine of evolution had not existed, palæontologists must have invented it, so irresistibly is it forced upon the mind by the study of the remains of the Tertiary Mammalia which have been brought to light since 1859.[3]

---

[1] *Ante*, p. 10.　　[2] *Coll. Essays*, ii. p. 226.　　[3] II. 241.

Huxley soon found that extinct animals also afforded play for his favourite inquiry into the architecture and affinities of organisms, and hence, in his hands, the fossil became, as it were, a living thing, bringing a message from the past. His inquiry into the character of some supposed fish-shields from the Downton sandstone, near Ludlow, led to the revolutionising of old theories concerning the earliest fishes. He showed that the huge creatures named, from the complex structure of their teeth, Labyrinthodonts, are allied to fishes, amphibians, and reptiles ; and if the intermediate forms between birds and reptiles are not so clearly traceable as he and others then held, his demonstration of the affinity between the two was one of his most brilliant successes.

One great consequence of these researches was that science was enriched by a clear demonstration of the many and close affinities between reptiles and birds, so that the two henceforth came to be known under the joint title of Sauropsida, the Amphibia being at the same time distinctly more separated from the reptiles, and their relations to fishes more clearly signified by the joint title of Ichthyopsida. At the same time proof was brought forward that the line of the descent of the Sauropsida clearly diverged from that of the Mammalia, both starting from some common ancestry. And besides this great generalisation, the importance of which, both from a classificatory and from an evolutional point of view, needs no comment, there came out of the same researches numerous lesser contributions to the advancement of morphological knowledge, including among others an attempt, in many respects successful, at a classification of birds.[1]

---

[1] "Obituary Notice of T. H. Huxley," by Sir Michael Foster. *Proc. Royal Society,* vol. lix.

But what will, perhaps, make closer appeal to the general inquirer, is the story of the fulfilment of Huxley's prophecy as to the discovery of the pedigree of the horse, which, down to 1870, had been traced to a three-toed ancestor.

The ungulate or hoofed quadrupeds are divided into the odd-toed and the even-toed, the toes never exceeding, except in the case of monstrosities, five on each limb. The horse, whose nearest allies in descent are the tapir and the rhinoceros, belongs to the odd-toed or Perissodactyla (Greek, *perissos*, uneven, and *daktulos*, finger). In the horse of to-day the toes have become absorbed, so that what is called its "knee" corresponds to the position of a man's wrist; the metacarpus, or "cannon-bone," answers to the third or middle finger of the human hand; the "pastern," "coronary," and "coffin" bones answer to the joints of that finger, and the hoof to its nail. The smaller, or "splint bones," represent our second and fourth fingers, and some small bony prominences at the bases of these probably represent our first and fifth fingers.[1]

Fossil remains of horses of the existing type are found as far back as the later Tertiary period; in the later Miocene or middle Tertiary beds, horse - like animals with three toes, the middle one of which touched the ground, have been discovered, while the early Miocene deposits have yielded an animal with

[1] On the general structure and modifications see *The Horse*, by Sir W. H. Flower, chaps. iii., iv.

horse-like characters having three complete toes. Here the European evidence comes to an end, and in summarising it in his presidential address to the Geological Society in 1870, Huxley said that—

if the expectation raised by the splints of the horses that, in some ancestors of the horses, these splints would be found to be complete digits, has been verified, we are furnished with very strong reasons for looking for a no less complete verification of the expectation that the three-toed *Plagiolophus*-like "avus" of the horse must have been a five-toed "atavus" at some early period.[1]

In 1876, when visiting America, he was shown by Professor Marsh the remarkable fossil found, among others, in the Eocene formations of North America, to which the name Orohippus was given, and which was then the oldest known "member of the equine series." It had four complete toes on the front limb, and three toes on the hind limb, besides other features linking it with the chain of equine ancestry. The discovery evidenced that the accepted theory of the European origin of the horse must be abandoned in favour of America, into which continent that animal, having become extinct, was imported by the Spaniards.

In commenting on this wonderful "find," in a lecture given at New York in September 1876, Huxley repeated the prophecy uttered six years before :—

The knowledge we now possess justifies us completely in the anticipation that, when the still lower Eocene deposits,

---

[1] *Coll. Essays*, viii. p. 361.

and those which belong to the Cretaceous period, have yielded up their remains of ancestral equine animals, we shall find, first, a form with four complete toes and a rudiment of the fifth digit in the hind foot ; while, in the older forms, the series of digits will be more and more complete until we come to the five-toed animals in which, if the doctrine of evolution is well-founded, the whole series must have taken its origin.[1]

The prophecy was fulfilled two months afterwards in Professor Marsh's discovery of complete skeletons of a five-toed animal in the early Eocene deposits at Wasatch in North America. The existence of the fossil form, which is named Phenacodus, was known to Professor Cope three years before by its teeth alone. The un-earthing of it, with all the bones in due place, the terminal bones of the toes showing that they were encased in hoofs, enabled palæontologists to assign it a place in the ungulate group, the type, as shown by the size of the brain-pan, being extremely low. "This," remarks Sir W. H. Flower, "is exactly in accord with what is now generally known of the progressive diminution of the size of the brain in all groups of animals the farther back we pass from the present time." [2]

Reference has been made already to the famous book in which Huxley demonstrates the physical and psychical identity of man and the higher apes with a completeness never before attempted, but the consideration of some of the effects of that demonstration will have more fitting place in the next chapter.

[1] *American Addresses*, p. 89.   [2] *The Horse*, p. 22.

Omitting any account of Huxley's minor discoveries, the last one of importance to be noted takes us back to 1878. In that year, while he was Fullerian Professor at the Royal Institution, he delivered a lecture on the origin of the skull in vertebrates.[1] In 1806, Oken, a German naturalist of somewhat dreamy type, when walking in the Hartz Forest, picked up the dried skull of a sheep, and the idea struck him that it was an expanded vertebral column. The priority of idea was, apparently with justice, claimed by Goethe, who saw in it a correlate to his theory of the "transformation of plants"—*i.e.*, that every part of a plant is made up of stem and leaf, modified for the particular function it has to perform. But what secured unquestioned belief in the view that the skull "is formed of a series of expanded vertebræ moulded together," was the support given to it by Owen, "who was at that time the leading vertebrate anatomist in England," and whose indorsement may be in some measure explained by the seeming accordance of the theory with his belief in "archetypal ideas."

Huxley, ever acting on his own maxim, "to regard the value of authority as neither greater nor less than as much as it can prove itself to be worth," was by no means convinced of the truth of the vertebral theory, since it lacked such confirmation as comparative embryology might be expected to supply. After examining a number of skulls of fishes, beasts, and men, he

[1] *Ante*, p. 17.

was satisfied that each skull is built upon a common plan, and that the primitive skull in the lowest or car-tilaginous fishes, where traces of the original vertebræ might be expected, "is an unsegmented gristly brain-box, and that in higher forms the vertebral nature of the skull cannot be thought of for a moment, since many of the bones, for example, those along the top of the skull, arise in the skin. . . . It may be true to say that there is a primitive identity of structure between the spinal or vertebral column and the skull, but it is no more true that the adult skull is a modified vertebral column than it would be to affirm that the vertebral column is a modified skull." This demolition of a hitherto unchallenged theory added to the strain on the relations between Owen and Huxley, but that minor result was of no moment to the latter, the larger issue of whose labours lay in the "marking an epoch in England in vertebrate morphology," and in "enunciating views which, if somewhat modified, are still, in the main, the views of the anatomists of to-day."[1]

Linnæus says that "fossils are not the children, but the parents, of rocks," and the interest aroused in the contents of the fossil-yielding rocks when Huxley went to the School of Mines was extended to the rocks them-selves. During his more official connection with the Geological Society as Deputy-President in 1862, and as President in 1869 and 1870, he delivered three ad-

---

[1] Sir Michael Foster, "Obituary Notice of T. H. Huxley," *Proc. Royal Society*, vol. lix.

dresses, each of which holds matter of permanent value. As already shown, the latest of these, which was entitled "Palæontology and the Doctrine of Evolution," dealt with the ancestry of the horse; but it embraced the more general question of the evidence as to intermediate links between species supplied by the fossiliferous rocks. This involved a revision of opinions expressed in the address of 1862, and the clear deliverance that Huxley entertained "no sort of doubt that the Reptiles, Birds, and Mammals of the Trias are the direct descendants of Reptiles, Birds, and Mammals which existed in the latter part of the Palæozoic epoch, but not in any area of the present dry land which has yet been explored by the geologist." In the 1862 address reference was made to the two facts established by palæontology : 1. That one and the same area of the earth's surface has been successively occupied by very different kinds of living beings; 2. That the order of succession established in one locality holds good, approximately, in all.

The inference which geologists had drawn from this was that wherever rocks containing the same kind of fossils are found in widely separated parts of the globe, they were formed at the same time. Correspondence in succession came to be looked upon as correspondence in age. Huxley, on the other hand, argued that the presence of fossils identical in type in distant rock-formations pointed to an opposite conclusion. On the theory of special creation the appearance of the same animal remains in the same order of strata in different zones was explicable. But on the theory of evolution considerable periods of time must have elapsed to permit of the migration of animals from place to place. Therefore, Huxley suggested that the ambiguous and misleading term "synchronism" should be discarded in favour of the term "homotaxial," as indicating that the presence of certain fossils in the same relative position in the succession of strata indicated a similarity of order, but not an identity of date.

In the 1869 address he discussed the interesting question of the age of the earth as determining the length of time which elapsed before it became cool enough to be the abode of life. On this question the physicists and the biologists were at issue.

At the outset the earth was a mass of glowing, incandescent gas, hurled-off, like its fellow-planets, from the vast nebula which was to condense into the solar system. Passing, under the continuous loss of heat, from the gaseous through the liquid and viscous to the solid state, it reached a degree of temperature which permitted of the existence of life upon its surface. The first living things were plants, and the carbon, which is an essential element in their structure, could not be detached from the atmosphere except at a temperature "somewhat above the freezing-point, and somewhat less than half-way to the boiling-point of water." Hence the question, At what period of its history did our globe, or that portion of it on which life first appeared (probably, as Buffon suggested, the polar area, as this would be the earliest to cool), arrive at that temperature? To this the mathematical physicists, at the head of whom stands Lord Kelvin, essayed answer, the data for which were supplied—1, by the rate at which the earth parted with its store of heat; 2, by the decrease in the length of its day; and 3, by the time that the sun, as the source of life, has illuminated the earth. Of these, only the briefest summary is here possible. As to the first, Lord Kelvin (then Sir William Thomson) assumed that the matter of which the globe is made up is uniform throughout, and, therefore, that the rate at which it has parted with its heat is uniform. After hesitating between the statement that "the consolidation cannot have taken place less than twenty million years ago, nor more than four hundred million years ago," Lord Kelvin agreed that "some such period of time as one hundred million years ago" might be taken as a safely approximate estimate. As to the second, when the earth and moon were very near each other, the rotation was enormously quickened, and, as the moon retreated, the earth's rotation slowed, involving the gradual lengthening of the day. The retardation is due to the friction of the tides, which, under the pull of sun, and, in far greater degree, of moon, act as a brake upon the globe, increasing the day by about twenty-two seconds of time in every century. The period of the earth's habitability was reached when the day was approximately what it is now, permitting of the alternations of light and darkness, heat and cold, and other conditions now prevailing.

Lord Kelvin estimates "that the centrifugal force at the time of solidification cannot have been more than three per cent greater than it is at present, and, therefore, having regard to the known rate of retardation of the earth's rotation, this event occurred not more than one hundred million years ago."

As to the third, physicists are agreed that the maintenance of the sun's energy is to be explained as due to the heat generated by the falling-in and resulting collision of the particles of matter of which he is composed, involving the shrinkage of his diameter at the rate of two hundred and twenty feet yearly, or four miles per century. Lord Kelvin, admitting that "the estimates are necessarily very vague," is of opinion that "the sun may have already illuminated the earth for as many as one hundred million years; but it is almost certain that he has not illuminated the earth for five hundred million years."

Commenting on the indefiniteness of these and the foregoing estimates, Huxley aptly remarks that—

Mathematics may be compared to a mill of exquisite workmanship, which grinds you stuff in any degree of fineness, but, nevertheless, what you get out depends on what you put in; and as the grandest mill in the world will not extract wheat-flour from peascods, so pages of formulæ will not get a definite result out of loose data.[1]

But although some mathematicians of lesser calibre thought that Lord Kelvin had conceded too long a period, there was sufficient accord between them to make the biologists feel themselves in a tight place. Reckoning, from the rate at which materials, through the agency of rivers, are being deposited on ocean-bottoms, how long a time was necessary for the formation of the sedimentary rocks, and of rocks presumably within the life-period, the aggregate thickness of which is estimated at about fifty miles, they found the years allowed by the mathematicians wholly insufficient. Darwin was much concerned. Writing to Wallace in 1869, he says: "Thomson's views of the recent age of the world have been for some time one of my sorest troubles;" and again, in 1871, "I can say nothing more about missing links than what I have said. I should rely much on pre-Silurian times; but then comes Sir W. Thomson, like an odious spectre." Huxley was in no wise disturbed.

Biology [he said] takes her time from geology. The only reason we have for believing in the slow rate of the change in living forms is the fact that they persist through a series of deposits which, geology informs us, have taken a long while to make. If the geological clock is wrong, all the naturalist will have to do is to modify his notions of the rapidity of change accordingly. And I venture to point out that when we are told that the limitation of the period during which living beings have inhabited this planet to one, two, or three hundred million years requires a complete revolution in geological speculation, the *onus probandi* rests on the maker of the assertion, who brings forward not a shadow of evidence in its support.[1]

---

[1] *Lay Sermons*, p. 213.

Meantime, occasion was given to eager adversaries to say, "Behold how good and how pleasant a thing it is to see this discord!" and it is not surprising that the hope was nurtured in the minds of many that so serious a disagreement would in some way wreck the doctrine of evolution. That reluctant convert to the theory of the mutability of species, Lord Salisbury, did not fail to press home the difficulty in his Presidential Address to the British Association. After referring to the "penurious spirit" shown by Professor Tait in cutting down Lord Kelvin's estimate of one hundred million years to ten million years, he chaffed their opponents with revelling in the prodigality of the ciphers which they put at the end of the earth's hypothetical life.

Long cribbed and cabined within the narrow bounds of the popular chronology, they have exulted wantonly in their new freedom. They have lavished their millions of years with the open hand of a prodigal heir indemnifying himself by present extravagance for the enforced self-denial of his youth. But it cannot be gainsaid that their theories require at least all this elbow-room. If we think of that vast distance over which Darwin conducts us from the jelly-fish lying on the primeval beach to man as we know him now; if we reflect that the prodigious change requisite to transform one into the other is made up of a chain of generations, each advanc-ing by a minute variation from the form of its predecessor, and if we further reflect that these successive changes are so minute that in the course of our historical period—say three thousand years—this progressive variation has not advanced by a single step perceptible to our eyes, in respect to man or the animals and plants with which man is familiar, we shall admit that for a chain of change so vast, of which the smallest link is longer than our recorded history, the biologists are making no extravagant claim when they demand at least many hundred million years for the accomplishment of the stupendous process. Of course, if the mathematicians are right, the biologists cannot have what they demand. If, for the purposes of their theory, organic life must have existed on the globe more than a hundred million years ago, it must, under the temperature then prevailing, have existed in a state of vapour. The jelly-fish would have been dissipated in steam long before he had had a chance of displaying the advantageous variation which was to make him the ancestor of the human race. I see, in the eloquent discourse of one of my most recent and most distinguished predecessors in this chair, Sir Archibald Geikie, that the controversy is still alive. The mathematicians sturdily adhere to their figures, and the biologists are quite sure the mathematicians must have made a mistake. I will not get myself into the line of fire by intervening in such a controversy. But until it is adjusted the laity may be excused for returning a verdict of " not proven " upon the wider issues the Darwinian school has raised.[1]

Lord Salisbury unwittingly helped the cause which his instincts prompted him to hinder. With that prevision of the seer in combination with the skill of the discoverer, which is the possession only of the rarer spirits of our kind, Huxley had pierced the core of the matter when he asked, " Is the earth nothing but a cooling mass, ' like a hot-water jar, such as is used in carriages,' or ' a globe of sandstone,' and has its cooling been uniform ? " And incited thereto by Lord Salisbury's Address, provocative as it was of discussion on so many sides, Professor Perry, who held the common opinion that it was " hopeless to expect that Lord Kelvin should

[1] *Times*, 9th August 1894.

have made an error in calculation," examined the subject, not "to substitute a more correct age for that
obtained by Lord Kelvin, but rather to show that the
data from which the true age could be calculated are
not really available." The result of that examination
was to challenge Lord Kelvin's assumption of a uniform
state of the materials of the globe, and to show that " its
interior may be of better conducting material than the
surface rock," whereby the cooling of that surface to a
habitable condition would be enormously quickened,
and the life-period pushed back to the four hundred
million years required by the geologists and biologists.
The details of the process by which Professor Perry
arrived at his conclusions are too technical and lengthy
for reproduction here,[1] and, moreover, it suffices to quote
Lord Kelvin's admission that his estimate may be insufficient. "I thought," he says in a letter to *Nature*,
" my range from twenty millions to four hundred millions
was probably wide enough ; but it is quite possible that I
should have put the superior limit a good deal higher,
perhaps four thousand instead of four hundred."[2] *Apropos*
of Professor Perry's results, Huxley wrote in a private
letter, under date of 6th November 1894 : "I am so
much out of the world now that I had not heard of the
' rift within the lute' of the mathematicians. But that a
big crack would show itself sooner or later I have never
doubted."

[1] For these, see *Nature*, 3rd January 1895 ; 24th September 1896.
[2] *Nature*, 3rd January 1895.

It would be easy to fill many pages of this little
volume with a summarised account of Huxley's original
work in biology alone, but the examples chosen may be
taken to constitute his chief claim to the title of discoverer. They may suffice to show, in the words of the
tribute paid to him by Sir Michael Foster and Professor
E. Ray Lankester in their preface to the collection of his
Scientific Memoirs, that, " apart from the influence exerted
by his popular writings, the progress of biology during
the present century was largely due to labours of his of
which the general public knew nothing, and that he was
in some respects the most original and most fertile in
discovery of all his fellow-workers in the same branch of
science." [1]

[1] Vol. I. p. vi. (1898).

III.

THE INTERPRETER.

In an essay on the *Origin of Species*, written in 1860, Huxley admits that two years before then "the position of the supporters of the special creation theory seemed more impregnable than ever, if not by its own inherent strength, at any rate by the obvious failure of all the attempts which had been made to carry it."[1] If it was discarded, there was nothing to replace it; hence, like institutions for the reform or abolition of which the time is not ripe, it existed on sufferance. Emphasis of this fact is necessary for full understanding of the revolution whereby old things passed away and all things became new.

Huxley was a boy of twelve when Darwin, on his return to England, opened his "first note-book for facts in relation to the origin of species," speculation about the possible modification of which had been incited by his observations on past and present life-forms on the South American continent. Fifteen

[1] *Coll. Essays*, ii. p. 69.

months afterwards, in October 1838, he read for amuse-ment *Malthus on Population*, and he says :—

> Being well prepared to appreciate the struggle for existence which everywhere goes on, from long-continued observations of the habits of plants and animals, it at once struck me that under these circumstances favourable variations would tend to be preserved, and unfavourable ones destroyed. The result of this would be the formation of new species.[1]

In 1842 he put his theory into shape, then enlarged his manuscript from time to time, and with that un-paralleled patience which controlled all his researches, went on collecting masses of facts and weighing the evidence deducible from them, not venturing to make known, save to his most intimate friends, his convic-tions as to the mutability of species. It seemed "like confessing a murder," he said. And so the matter drifted until 1858, when there came to him from Dr Alfred Russel Wallace, who was living at Ternate, an island in the Malay Archipelago, a communication in which his own theory was propounded, and in such coincidence of terms that Darwin told Lyell if Wallace had had his MS. sketch of 1842, "he could not have made a better short abstract."[2] To complete the parallel, Wallace also was led to think of "positive checks" by reading Parson Malthus. After conferring with Hooker and Lyell, both of whom had seen Darwin's abstract some years before, it was arranged that Wallace's paper and a *précis* of Darwin's manuscript should be read at a meet-

[1] Darwin's *Life and Letters*, i. p. 83.   [2] *Ib.*, ii. p. 116.

ing of the Linnean Society, which was held on 1st July
1858.[1] Hooker says that the interest excited was in-
tense, but no discussion, only desultory talk, "with
bated breath," followed the reading, and the matter
caused no commotion outside a limited circle.

Huxley does not appear to have been present, and it
is doubtful if he knew aught of the proceedings save by
hearsay. For, writing to Hooker on 5th September
1858, he says, "Wallace's impetus seems to have set
Darwin going in earnest, and I am rejoiced to hear we
shall learn his views in full, at last. I look forward
to a great revolution being effected."[2] And, in his
lecture "On the Persistent Types of Animal Life,"
delivered at the Royal Institution on 3rd June 1859,
there is no reference to the Darwin-Wallace theory,
only allusion to the

hypothesis which supposes the species of living beings living
at any time to be the result of the gradual modification of
pre-existing species—a hypothesis which, though unproven
and sadly damaged by some of its supporters, is yet the only
one to which physiology lends any countenance.[3]

He was not a convert till the book appeared. "What
will Huxley say?" is the burden of Darwin's letters.
"I am intensely curious to hear Huxley's opinion of my
book." "If I can convert Huxley I shall be content."

[1] An excellent abstract of the joint Memoir is given by Professor
E. B. Poulton in his *Charles Darwin*, pp. 65-78.
[2] I. 159.   [3] *Scient. Memoirs*, ii. p. 90.

"I long to hear what Huxley thinks."[1] Ten days after this, in a letter dated 23rd November 1859, Huxley, to whom an advance copy had been sent, tells Darwin that he is "prepared to go to the stake, if requisite," for the doctrine of natural selection, and, scenting the battle from afar, adds: "I am sharpening up my claws and beak in readiness for defence of the 'noble book.'" Darwin was made happy. He had converted the chief of doubters, to whom he replied: "Like a good Catholic who has received extreme unction, I can now sing 'Nunc dimittis.' I should have been more than contented with one quarter of what you have said."[2]

Huxley was satisfied that Darwin "had demonstrated a true cause for the production of species." In a course of lectures to working men delivered in 1863, he said:—

I really believe that the alternative is either Darwinism or nothing, for I do not know of any rational conception or theory of the organic universe which has any scientific position at all beside Mr Darwin's. . . . Whatever may be the objections to his views, certainly all other theories are absolutely out of court.[3]

But doubting, as was his wont, "whatever could be doubted," he was not satisfied that the evidence

[1] *Life and Letters*, ii. pp. 176, 221, 225. What Huxley did think, after mastering the central idea of the book, was, "How extremely stupid not to have thought of that!"—*Ib.*, p. 197.
[2] *Ib.*, p. 232.   [3] *Coll. Essays*, ii. p. 467.

was in all respects complete.   He held that full proof
would be obtained only when experiments in selective
breeding from a common stock resulted in the production of varieties more or less infertile with one
another.   In his article on the "Origin of Species"
in the *Westminster Review* of April 1860, he says:—

After much consideration, and with assuredly no bias
against Mr Darwin's views, it is our clear conviction that,
as the evidence stands, it is not absolutely proven that a
group of animals, having all the characters exhibited by
species in nature, has ever been originated by selection,
whether artificial or natural.   Groups having the morphological character of species—distinct and permanent races,
in fact—have been so produced over and over again ; but
there is no positive evidence at present that any group of
animals has, by variation and selective breeding, given rise
to another group which was even in the least degree infertile with the first.   Mr Darwin is perfectly aware of this
weak point, and brings forward a number of ingenious and
important arguments to diminish the force of the objection.
We admit the value of these arguments to their fullest
extent—nay, we will go so far as to express our belief that
experiments conducted by a skilful physiologist ("instead
of by a mere breeder," he adds in a letter to Darwin[1])
would very probably obtain the desired production of mutu-
ally more or less infertile breeds from a common stock in a
comparatively few years.   But still, as the case stands at
present, this "little rift within the lute" is not to be disguised or overlooked.[2]

Twenty-seven years afterwards, Huxley referred to
the insecurity of the logical foundation as remaining
in the absence of experiments with the results de-

[1] I. 195 ; and cf. *ib.*, 239.   [2] *Coll. Essays*, ii. p. 75.

manded; nevertheless, in the last speech which he delivered in public, a few months before his death, he expressed his unshaken belief in the theory

propounded by Mr Darwin thirty-four years ago as the only hypothesis at present put before us which has a sound scientific foundation.[1]

It may not be out of place to quote some suggestive observations on Huxley's contention from an article on the *Life and Letters* in a recent number of his whilom antagonist, but now appreciative, if not whole-hearted, disciple, the *Quarterly Review*:—

It is not difficult to understand the mutual sterility of natural species as an incidental result of their separation for an immense period of time. In the process of fertilisation a portion of a single cell-nucleus from one individual fuses with a portion from another individual, the two combining to form the complete nucleus of the first cell of the offspring, from which all the countless cells of the future individual will arise by division. Each part-nucleus contains the whole of the hereditary qualities received from and through its respective parent, and must therefore be of inconceivable complexity. We can only speak in generalities of processes of which so little is known; but we cannot be wrong in assuming that sterility is sometimes due to the fact that the complexity of the one part-nucleus fails in some way to suit the complexity of the other. . . . The length of time required for mutual sterility to be complete may be inferred from the fact that entirely distinct, but closely related, species are still partially fertile in that they can produce hybrid offspring. When our domestic breeds of pigeons have been entirely prevented from interbreeding for

[1] II. 389.

some immense period of time, we may expect that they too
will only produce sterile hybrids, and, later still, not even
these. At present the majority of these breeds are not
everywhere rigidly prevented from interbreeding, so that an
approximation to natural species-formation has not even
begun. There are others, however, such as the most widely
different breeds of dogs, in which the divergence in size is
so extreme that interbreeding has probably been a mechanical impossibility for some considerable time.[1]

Huxley's letters express dissent from the so-called
"Neo-Lamarckian" school, represented by Mr Herbert
Spencer, which contends that the use and disuse of
organs, together with the action of surroundings, produce modifications of structure which are transmitted
to offspring. There are no specific references to Professor Weismann's *Essays in Heredity* (1883), in which,
representing the so-called "Neo-Darwinian" school,
natural selection, acting on favourable variations, is
held to be all-sufficient for the production of new
species ; but, in June 1886, Huxley wrote to Mr
Spencer as follows :—

Mind, I have no *a priori* objection to the transmission of
functional modifications whatever. In fact, as I told you,
I should rather like it to be true.

But I argued against the assumption (with Darwin, as I
do with you) of the operation of a factor which, if you will
forgive me for saying so, seems as far off support by trust-
worthy evidence now as ever it was.[2]

To Mr Platt Ball he wrote in 1890 :—

I absolutely disbelieve in use-inheritance as the evidence

[1] January 1901, pp. 269, 271.   [2] II. 133.

stands.   Spencer is bound to it *a priori*—his psychology goes to pieces without it.[1]

Huxley's researches in palæontology and embryology strengthened his conviction that " if all the conceptions promulgated in the *Origin of Species* which are peculiarly Darwinian were swept away, the theory of evolution of plants and animals would not be in the slightest degree shaken."[2]   For him the importance of that book lay in its influence beyond the limits of its theory, which dealt only with living things.   This is put with his usual clearness and vigour in his chapter on its reception in Darwin's *Life and Letters*, and explains his place as foremost champion :—

The oldest of all philosophies was bound hand and foot, and cast into utter darkness, during the millennium of theological scholasticism.   But Darwin poured new life-blood into the ancient frame ; the bonds burst, and the revivified thought of ancient Greece has proved itself to be a more adequate expression of the universal order of things than any of the schemes which have been accepted by the credulity, and welcomed by the superstition, of seventy later generations of men.

To any one who studies the signs of the times, the emergence of the philosophy of Evolution, in the attitude of claimant to the throne of the world of thought, from the limbo of hatred, and, as many hoped, forgotten things, is the most portentous event of the nineteenth century.   But the most effective weapons of the modern champions of Evolution were fabricated by Darwin ; and the *Origin of Species* has enlisted a formidable body of combatants,

---

[1] II. 268.   [2] *Nature,* 1st Nov. 1894.

trained in the severe school of Physical Science, whose ears might have long remained deaf to the speculations of *a priori* philosophers.[1]

In this same chapter Huxley makes a short reference, as to a storm whose tumult has long been stilled, leaving only a ground-swell, to the "years which had to pass away before misrepresentation, ridicule, and denunciation ceased to be the most notable constituents of the majority of the multitudinous criticisms of the *Origin of Species.*" What he touches upon with brevity need not be amplified here. It would fail to interest an age which, lightly valuing the intellectual freedom won for it, but not by it, is without enthusiasm, without aspiration, save as these are moved by ignoble lust of empire or by enervating craving after luxury; an age in which "the coarsest political standard is undoubtingly and finally applied over the whole realm of human thought, . . . in which the souls of men have become void, while into the void have entered in triumph the seven devils of Secularity."[2]

But the remnant who care to know through what tribulation the fighters in the sixties entered the kingdom of the free may be told that the battle was the fiercer by reason of divisions in the camp of science, whereas the theologians were a solid phalanx. True it is that one of the earliest converts to Darwinism was a clerical ornithol-

[1] II. p. 180; and cf. *Coll. Essays*, i. p. 43; ix. p. 104. "Classical history is a part of modern history: it is medieval history which is ancient."—Bagehot's *Physics and Politics*, p. 169.

[2] *On Compromise*, by John Morley, pp. 14, 37.

ogist, Canon Tristram (still with us), who applied the theory of natural selection to explanation of the colours of birds of the Sahara. Charles Kingsley, too, was sympathetic; but these were as men "born out of due time." Owen's malignant attitude has had reference; Sir John Herschel said that natural selection was "the law of higgledy-piggledy," the exact meaning of which, Darwin confessed, puzzled him, as well it might; Adam Sedgwick read parts of the book with "absolute sorrow, as false and grievously mischievous." But he hoped to meet Darwin "in heaven." Whewell's opposition took the form of refusing the *Origin of Species* a place in the library of Trinity College; Lyell at first, and Carpenter, with others, throughout, accepted with reservations; while the tone of the more intellectual organs was reflected in the *Athenæum*, for long years an anti-Darwinian journal. Touching on the theological issues involved, it committed Darwin "to the tender mercies of the Divinity Hall, the College, the Lecture-room, and the Museum."

On both sides of the Atlantic the drum ecclesiastic was beaten in pulpits where, needless to say, vituperative rhetoric did duty for argument; preachers in cathedrals and little Bethels were at one in condemnation of a "brutal philosophy" whose success meant the denial of Scripture and the dethronement of God; while Episcopacy voiced itself through the Bishop of Oxford's philippic in the *Quarterly Review*, which, albeit inspired by Owen, exhibited "preposterous incapacity" in dealing with elementary biology.

There was only one man qualified to take up the gauntlet. Huxley's prominence as the most capable interpreter and best-equipped defender of the Darwinian theory dates from the British Association Meeting of 1860. *Apropos* of some friction with Owen in 1852, he said, in a letter to his sister, that he was "quite ready to fight half-a-dozen dragons." He was then writing for his living, and, referring to his jealous rival's "bitter pen," he adds, "I flatter myself that, on occasion, I can match him in that department." [1] Eight years after, the serious issues between himself and the anti-Darwinians added to his eagerness for the fray *unguibus et rostro*. This was gratified by the opportunity for exercise of a pen never dipped in malice. By a happy chance the columns of the *Times* were opened to him for a review of the *Origin of Species*. The book had been sent to Mr Lucas, a member of the staff, who "was as innocent of any knowledge of science as a babe," and who, at the suggestion of a friend, passed-on the copy to Huxley, stipulating only that he should preface the article with a few sentences. The review appeared on 26th December 1859, and thereby Huxley secured the aid of the then influential paper in "giving the book a fair start with the multitudinous readers of the leading journal"—"the educated mob who derive their ideas from the *Times*," as he said in a letter to Hooker. [2] The review is re-printed in the second volume of *Collected Essays*, in which, under the title "Darwiniana," are included allied

[1] I. 98.   [2] I. 177.

articles expository of the doctrine of natural selection, which had appeared in serials or were based upon popular lectures. They were needed, since "exposition was not Darwin's *forte*, and his English is sometimes wonderful."[1]

The *Origin of Species* is not easy reading. Thirty years after its publication, when Huxley, of all men, might have been expected to have mastered it from title to colophon, he said in a letter to Hooker, "It is one of the hardest books to understand thoroughly that I know of."[2]

Darwin, recluse by temperament and frail health, content, in the quiet of his Kentish home, to continue his work of collecting and verifying, was no controversialist. Hence the preaching of the new doctrine and the fighting for it fell to "my general agent,"[3] as he called Huxley; to "Darwin's bull - dog," as Huxley called himself.[4] Not returning railing for railing, but fact-supported argument for epithet; albeit sometimes answering "a fool according to his folly," Huxley made it his chief business to enlarge to the full the hint which, at the end of the *Origin of Species*, Darwin threw out in a brief sentence : "Much light will be thrown on the origin of man and his history." Darwin's desire not to unduly prejudice the minds of readers to whom his theory was wholly new by too plain an indication of its bearing, and his anxiety to advance no statement without complete in-

---

[1] II. 190.   [2] II. 192.
[3] Darwin's *Life and Letters*, ii. p. 251.   [4] I. 363.

vestment of fact, explain his reticence. But it needed no great acuteness on the part of a critical reader to see that the subject could not be thus selvedged. *The Descent of Man* was the logical supplement to the *Origin of Species*; but it was not published until 1871. Explaining in 1894 the position which he took up in 1860, Huxley says :—

Among the many problems which came under my consideration, the position of the human species in zoological classification was one of the most serious. Indeed, at that time it was a burning question, in the sense that those who touched it were almost certain to burn their fingers severely. . . . Even among those who considered man from the point of view, not of vulgar prejudice, but of science, opinions lay poles asunder. Linnæus had taken one view, Cuvier another; and among my senior contemporaries, men like Lyell, regarded by many as revolutionaries of the deepest dye, were strongly opposed to anything which tended to break down the barrier between man and the rest of the animal world.

Huxley then refers to his own hesitation upon the matter, until Owen's assertion as to certain fundamental differences of structure in the brain of man and ape[1] led him to reinvestigate the subject, with the result that he was satisfied as to the structures in question not being peculiar to man, " but shared by him with all the higher, and many of the lower apes."

Matters were at this point when the *Origin of Species* appeared.

The weighty sentence, " Light will be thrown on the origin of man and his history," was not only in full harmony

---

[1] *Ante*, p. 18.

with the conclusions at which I had arrived, but was strongly supported by them. And inasmuch as Development and Vertebrate Anatomy were not among Mr Darwin's many specialities, it appeared to me that I should not be intruding on the ground he had made his own if I discussed this part of the general question. In fact, I thought that I might probably serve the cause of Evolution by doing so.[1]

In the spring of 1861 he gave a course of weekly lectures to working men, " On the Relation of Man to the rest of the Animal Kingdom." This was followed by an invitation from the Philosophical Institution of Edinburgh to deliver two lectures upon the same subject. As " it was only a few years since that the electors to the Chair of Natural History in a famous northern university had refused to invite a very distinguished man to occupy it because he advocated the doctrine of the diversity of species of mankind," Huxley was not prepared for the applause with which the Edinburgh audience greeted the statement that he entertained " no doubt of the origin of man from the same stock as the apes." But there were shouts of dissent outside the lecture hall. The local press was furious at the reception accorded to that " anti-scriptural and most debasing theory, . . . standing in blasphemous contradiction to Biblical narrative and doctrine." There should have been deep resentment at this " foul outrage committed upon them individually and upon the whole species as ' made in the likeness of God,' by deserting the hall in a body, or using some more emphatic form of protest against the corruption of

[1] II. 178.

youth by the vilest and beastliest paradox ever vented in
ancient or modern times amongst Pagans or Christians." [1]
Thus wrote the *Witness*, invective, as usual, doing duty
for argument; while the *Scotsman*, as Huxley told Darwin,
was "more scurrilously personal, and more foolish."

The two sets of lectures formed the basis of *Evidence
as to Man's Place in Nature*, published in 1863. The
third section of the book dealt with the question of
fossil human remains, concerning which Lyell had asked
for information when preparing his *Antiquity of Man*.
Well anathematised by the reviewers, the "old stupid
Athenæum," as Darwin called it, telling its readers that
"Lyell's object is to make man old, Huxley's to degrade
him," the book had an immediate success. It remains
a classic on the subject, because, as Mr Chalmers
Mitchell remarks, "the advance of knowledge has only
added to the details of the argument; it has not made
any reconstruction of it necessary." [2]

An outline of the chapter describing the manlike
apes, and explaining the likenesses and differences between them and man, may help to make clear how
inevitable was a controversy in which Huxley took
the chief part.

It is obvious that, in any classification of animals
founded on external resemblances, both empiric and
expert would agree in grouping the monkeys, those
"blurred copies," often caricatures, of man, with him.
And "the great law-giver of systematic zoology,"

Linnæus, places man and the four anthropoid or man-like apes—the chimpanzee, gorilla, orang-utan, and gibbon—at the head of the Primates, the name given by him to the highest members of the Vertebrate class.   The chimpanzee and gorilla are sometimes grouped as of the same genus, but the orang-utan and gibbon are undoubtedly distinct genera.   They are found only in the old world—the chimpanzee and gorilla inhabiting tropical Africa, and the orang-utan and gibbon south-eastern Asia and the Malay Archipelago.   They are tailless, semi-erect, long-armed, the aperture of the nostrils pointing downwards, whence the term catarrhine ; they are arboreal in their habits, and, mainly, vegetarians.

The *Chimpanzee* is about five feet in height, nearly black, like the negro, has arms which reach below the knee, and a slightly curved backbone. (The S-like shape of man's backbone is one of the co-operating causes of his erect position, stability being thereby given to the structure, so that nine times as great a vertical force is required to bend it as if it had been straight. The backbone of the savage is less curved than that of civilised man.)   The chimpanzee has one pair of ribs more than man.   The feet are flat-soled, and shorter than the hands, and have an opposable toe, which, in all the anthropoids, acts as a thumb, the feet being used for climbing and grasping.   The fingers of the hand are long and powerful, but the thumb is smaller than that of a man, with the lines and furrows on whose hand

those on the hand of the ape correspond. The im-
postors who ply the trade of palmistry may note this
fact, either for the purpose of reading the fate and
fortune of the anthropoids, or, what would be equally
reasonable in the case of their dupes, determining the
future of these from the creases in their trousers.
The skull of the chimpanzee approximates nearest
among the anthropoids to man's, and the brain, which
is half the size of his, has the same ridges or convolutions, although, in proportion, these are simpler and
larger. The number of teeth in man and the manlike
apes is the same, but in the latter the canines are longer.
The chimpanzee makes its nest in trees, swinging from
branch to branch to a great distance, and leaping with
astonishing agility. "It is not unusual to see the 'old
folks' sitting under a tree regaling themselves with fruit
and friendly chat, while their 'children' are leaping
around them, and swinging from tree to tree with
boisterous merriment." [1]

The *Gorilla* is the largest and most savage of the
four. It is about five feet and a half in height; its
body is massive and powerful, and covered with coarse
black hair. The arms reach to the middle of the leg,
and, of all the anthropoids, the feet and hands most
approximate to those of man. It has very long canine
teeth, although these are relatively smaller than in the
primitive mammal. Its ponderous body renders it less
agile for arboreal life, hence it dwells chiefly on the

[1] Dr Savage, quoted in *Man's Place in Nature*, p. 43 (1863).

ground, resting its arms on the knuckles of the hands as it shambles along in a half-swinging motion. The gorillas live in bands, but are not so numerous as the chimpanzees : the females generally exceed the males in number. " My informants all agree in the assertion that but one adult male is seen in a band; that when the young males grow up a contest takes place for mastery, and the strongest, by killing and driving out the others, establishes himself as the head of the community." [1]

The *Orang-utan* is about four feet in height. Its body is bulky and powerful, and reddish - brown in colour, like that of the Malay native. The backbone is slightly curved; the feet are longer than the hands, and the arms reach to the ankles. Its brain approximates nearest of all the anthropoids to that of man in structure and appearance. It is a slow and cautious climber, but on all - fours it can, for a time, outstrip a man in running. Like the gorilla, it defends itself with its hands. It is wholly arboreal, making nests for itself and family, the young remaining for some time under the mother's protection. In reading Dr Alfred Russel Wallace's account of a baby orang-utan, the late John Fiske was struck by the fact that it had an infancy which is a great deal longer than that of some lower mammals, but which was very brief compared with that of the period of human infancy. Twenty-five centuries ago Anaximander remarked that " while other animals quickly find food for themselves, man alone

[1] *Man's Place in Nature,* p. 49.

requires a prolonged period of suckling." Looking at this fact under the light of evolution, the theory suggested itself to Mr Fiske that the comparatively long duration of human infancy is a condition of human intelligence, the period, moreover, being longer in the civilised man than in the savage. While in all other animals, in descending scale, little remains to be developed after birth, in man it is precisely the reverse. The period during which he remains helpless or dependent upon others fills a large portion of his life. Puppies, kittens, and colts are born fully equipped with all the nervous apparatus by which they can shift for themselves : they have nothing to learn from, or to add to, the stock of inherited qualities. One generation succeeds another in unprogressive monotony. Whereas, in man, the period during which the nerve-connections and their correlative associations necessary for self-maintenance are being formed lengthens as intelligence becomes more complex. From this much of great import follows. For it is this long, helpless period of human infancy, involving dependence on the parents, which begets the solicitude, the sympathy, and the self-denial of which the strands of family life are woven. Carried further, there is the development of those regardful feelings for others, and of that self-restraint, which results in the extension of the family unit to the social unit, all which lie at the base of ethics.

The *Gibbon*, smallest and gentlest of the four, is about three feet in height. Its arms touch the ground

when it is erect; the soles of the feet turn inward, a
feature explained by their arboreal functions, and concerning which Professor Osborn reports a droll remark
of Huxley's.   He said, "When a fond mother calls
upon me to admire her baby, I never fail to respond;
and while cooing appropriately, I take advantage of any
opportunity to gently ascertain whether the soles of its
feet turn in, and tend to support my theory of arboreal
descent." [1]   The chest of the gibbon approximates nearest
to that of man's, and it has callosities or sitting-pads on
the buttocks.   It can run for some distance on its
feet, but it lives in tall trees, and is a rapid leaper,
springing as much as forty feet from tree to tree.   Like
the chimpanzee, it fights with its teeth.

In contrast and resemblance to these four anthropoid
apes is *man*, "erect and featherless biped," between
whom and his semi-erect and hairy congeners there is
no fundamental differences in structure, the variations
being no greater than in any other allied group of
animals.   It is true that no anatomist could mistake
the bones of a man for those of a gorilla; but the
differences between the one and the other are less than
those between a gorilla and the lowest Primates, say,
a lemur.   Like all other animals, the Primates originate
from a fertilised egg-cell; the primordial germ of a
man, a dog, a bird, a fish, a beetle, a snail, and a
polyp being in no essentially structural respects dis-
tinguishable.   Like all other vertebrates, the Primates

[1] II. 424.

pass through a period of embryonic development, in which the resemblances to one another are so closely the same both in outward and inward form and essentials of structure

that the differences between them are inconsiderable, while, in their subsequent course, they diverge more and more widely from one another. And it is a general law, that the more closely any animals resemble one another in adult structure, the longer and the more intimately do their embryos resemble one another; so that, for example, the embryos of a Snake and of a Lizard remain like one another longer than do those of a Snake and of a Bird; and the embryos of a Dog and of a Cat remain like one another for a far longer period than do those of a Dog and of a Bird, or of a Dog and an Opossum, or even than those of a Dog and a Monkey.

Thus the study of development affords a clear test of closeness of structural affinity, and one turns with impatience to inquire what results are yielded by the study of the development of Man. Is he something apart? Does he originate in a totally different way from Dog, Bird, Frog, and Fish, thus justifying those who assert him to have no place in nature and no real affinity with the lower world of animal life? Or does he originate in a similar germ, pass through the same slow and gradually progressive modification — depend upon the same contrivances for protection and nutrition, and finally enter the world by the help of the same mechanism? The reply is not doubtful for a moment, and has not been doubtful any time these thirty years. Without question, the mode of origin and the early stages of the development of man are identical with those of the animals immediately below him in the scale: without a doubt, in these respects, he is far nearer the Apes than the Apes are to the Dog. . . .

Identical in the physical processes by which he originates

—identical in the early stages of his formation—identical in the mode of his nutrition, before and after birth, with the animals which lie immediately below him in the scale—Man, if his adult and perfect structure be compared with theirs, exhibits, as might be expected, a marvellous likeness of organisation.   He resembles them as they resemble one another — he differs from them as they differ from one another. And though these differences and resemblances cannot be weighed and measured, their value may be readily estimated, the scale or standard of judgment, touching that value, being afforded and expressed by the system of classi-fication of animals now current among zoologists.[1]

In his general organisation man is most nearly allied to the Chimpanzee or the Gorilla (in mental capacity the Chimpanzee appears to be the nearer), and for the purposes of comparison, Huxley chose the Gorilla as "a brute now so celebrated in prose and verse" that "all must have formed some conception of his appearance." In dealing with the most important points of differ-ence between Man and Gorilla, he also contrasted the differences which separate the Gorilla from other Primates.

The differences in the body and limbs of Man and Gorilla at once strike the eye.   The trunk of the latter is larger, the lower limbs shorter, the upper limbs longer, and the brain-case smaller, than in Man.   In the "nobler and more characteristic organ," the skull, the differences are "immense."   The face of the Gorilla has massive jaw - bones and predominates over the brain-case; in Man these proportions are reversed.   The

[1] *Man's Place in Nature*, pp. 67, 68.

surface of the human skull is comparatively smooth, the
brow prominences or ridges project very little; in the
Gorilla "vast crests are developed upon the skull, and
the brow-ridges overhang the cavernous orbits like great
pent-houses. The smallest cranium observed in any
race of Man measures 63 cubic inches; while the most
capacious Gorilla skull measures not more than 34½
cubic inches. Striking as are these differences, their
force is somewhat impaired in view of the differences
between men themselves. The difference in the volume
of the cranial cavity of the various races of mankind is
far greater, absolutely, than that between the lowest
Man and the highest Ape, while, relatively, it is about
the same. For the largest human skull contained 114
cubic inches—that is to say, had very nearly double the
capacity of the smallest—while its absolute preponder-
ance of 51 cubic inches is far greater than that by which
the lowest adult male human cranium surpasses the
largest of the gorillas. After making all due allowance
for difference of size, the cranial capacities of some of
the lower apes fall nearly as much, relatively, below
those of the higher apes as the latter fall below man.
Thus, even in the important matter of cranial capacity,
Men differ more widely from one another than they do
from the Apes; while the lowest Apes differ as much,
in proportion, from the highest, as the latter does from
Man."[1] "What is true of these leading characteristics
of the skull holds good, as may be imagined, of all

[1] *Man's Place in Nature*, p. 78.

minor features; so that for every difference between the Gorilla's skull and the Man's, a similar constant difference of the same order (that is to say, consisting in excess or defect of the same quality) may be found between the Gorilla's skull and that of some other Ape. So that, for the skull, no less than for the skeleton in general, the proposition holds good, that the differences between Man and the Gorilla are of smaller value than those between the Gorilla and some other Apes."[1]

Reference has been made more than once to Owen's assertion that certain cerebral structures—the posterior lobe, the posterior cornu, and the hippocampus minor —are peculiar to man, and to the evidence adduced by Huxley, Flower, and other comparative anatomists in disproof of this, and if any justification of Huxley's denial of Owen's contention was needed, this will be found in Professor D. J. Cunningham's address to the Anthropological section of the British Association meeting of 1901. He says :—

To us, at the present time, it is difficult to conceive how it was ever possible to doubt that the occipital lobe was a distinctive character of the simian brain as well as of the human brain, and yet at successive meetings of the Association (1860, 1861, and 1862) a discussion, which was probably one of the most heated in the course of its history, took place on this very point. In the light of our present knowledge we could fully understand Professor Huxley closing the discussion by stating that the question had "become one of personal veracity." Indeed, the occipital lobe, so far from

---

[1] *Man's Place in Nature*, p. 81.

being absent, was developed in the ape to a relatively greater extent than in man, and this constituted one of the leading positive distinctive characters of the simian cerebrum.[1]

The advance in degree of complexity of brain-structure is traceable along the whole series of animals. In the Invertebrates the brain is a mass of nerve-ganglia near the head end of the body; in the lowest Vertebrate, the fish, it is very small, compared with the spinal cord; in reptiles its mass increases; and in birds it is still more marked. " The brain of the lowest Mammals, such as the duck-billed Platypus and the Opossums and Kangaroos, exhibits a still more definite advance in the same direction." A step higher in the scale, among the placental Mammals, the cerebral structure acquires a vast modification in the appearance of a new structure between the two halves of the brain, connecting them together.

In the lower and smaller forms of placental Mammals the surface of the cerebral hemispheres is either smooth or evenly rounded, or exhibits a very few grooves, which are technically termed " sulci," separating ridges or " convolutions" of the substance of the brain, and the smaller species of all orders tend to a similar smoothness of brain. But, in the higher orders, and especially the larger members of these orders, the grooves or sulci become extremely numerous, and the intermediate convolutions proportionately more complicated in their meanderings, until, in the Elephant, the Porpoise, the higher Apes, and Man, the cerebral surface appears a perfect labyrinth of tortuous foldings.[2] . . . The surface of the brain of a monkey exhibits a sort of skeleton map of man's, and in the manlike apes the details become more and more filled in until it is only in minor characters, such

---

[1] *Times*, Sept. 14, 1901.   [2] *Man's Place in Nature*, p. 96.

as the greater excavation of the anterior lobes, the constant presence of fissures usually absent in man, and the different disposition and proportions of some convolutions that the Chimpanzee's or the Orang's brain can be structurally distinguished from Man's.[1]

It must not be overlooked, however, that there is a very striking difference in absolute mass and weight between the lowest human brain and that of the highest ape, a difference which is all the more remarkable when we recollect that a full-grown Gorilla is probably pretty nearly twice as heavy as a Bosjes man, or as many a European woman. It may be doubted whether a healthy human adult brain ever weighed less than 31 or 32 ounces, or that the heaviest gorilla brain has exceeded 20 ounces. This is a very noteworthy circumstance, and doubtless will one day help to furnish an explanation of the great gulf which intervenes between the lowest man and the highest ape in intellectual power; but it has little systematic value for the simple reason that, as may be concluded from what has been already said respecting cranial capacity, the difference in weight of brain between the highest and the lowest men is far greater, both relatively and absolutely, than that between the lowest man and the highest ape. The latter, as has been seen, is represented by, say, 12 ounces of cerebral substance absolutely, or by 32 : 20 relatively; but as the largest recorded human brain weighed between 65 and 66 ounces, the former difference is represented by more than 33 ounces absolutely, or by 65 : 32 relatively. Regarded systematically, the cerebral differences of man and apes are not of more than generic value—his family distinction resting chiefly on his dentition, his pelvis, and his lower limbs.

Thus, whatever system of organs be studied, the comparison of their modifications in the ape series leads to one and the same result—that the structural differences which separate Man from the Gorilla and the Chimpanzee are not so great as those which separate the gorilla from the lower apes.[2]

---

[1] *Man's Place in Nature*, p. 100.   [2] *Ib.*, p. 103.

After thus showing that no line of separation can be drawn between man and the animals beneath him, structurally considered, Huxley added his " belief that the attempt to draw a psychical distinction is equally futile, and that even the highest faculties of feeling and of intellect begin to germinate in lower forms of life." [1]

For, in all the higher mammals, the structure and functions of the nervous system are, fundamentally, the same ; in the minutest microscopical details, the sense-organs, the nerves, the spinal cord, and the brain of a dog, an elephant, and an ape correspond to the same organs in man. If any part of the mental apparatus is injured or thrown out of gear, the result is the same in each case—functional disturbance or suspense. The dog and the horse behave as we behave ; nor can this be otherwise, since their sense-organs report, of course with vast differences of result, to their central nervous systems the messages that are transmitted by like apparatus to ours, and, within the limits of their consciousness, they are affected as we are affected, and their actions are ruled accordingly. " If there is no ground for believing that a dog thinks, neither is there any for believing that he feels." To those familiar with the ways of animals, there is no need to labour the point, and, " in short," as Huxley says—

It seems hard to assign any good reason for denying to the

---

[1] *Man's Place in Nature*, p. 109.

higher animals any mental state, or process, in which the employment of the vocal or visual symbols of which language is composed is not involved ; and comparative psychology confirms the position in relation to the rest of the animal world assigned to man by comparative anatomy. As comparative anatomy is easily able to show that, physically, man is but the last term of a long series of forms which lead, by slow gradations, from the highest mammal to the almost formless speck of living protoplasm which lies on the shadowy boundary between animal and vegetable life ; so comparative psychology, though but a young science, and far short of her elder sister's growth, points to the same conclusion.[1]

Nevertheless, the gulf which separates the man from the ape, and from animals whose intelligence excels that of the ape, is vast and impassable. Its vastness prevents some among the qualified few, and of course the majority of the prejudiced or ill-informed, from accepting the fact of a common origin of animal and human mental faculties. Among those who walked one mile with Darwin, but refused to go "twain," the most notable is Dr Alfred Russel Wallace, the co-propounder of the theory of natural selection. He contends that man's spiritual and intellectual nature "must have had another origin, and for this origin we can only find adequate cause in the unseen universe of spirit." In like manner, the late Professor St George Mivart, while admitting that man's body "was evolved from pre-existing material," asserted that "his soul was created in quite a different way . . . by the direct action of the Almighty."[2] And in a lecture on the functions of the brain, the late Sir James

[1] *Coll. Essays*, vi. p. 125.   [2] *Genesis of Species*, p. 325.

Paget contended that man's possession of reason and conscience

establish between him and the brutes a great difference, not in degree alone, but in kind.   The spirit differs from all the faculties in its independence of our organisation, for it is exercised best in complete abstraction from all that is sensible : it is wholly independent of the organisation of the brain, wholly independent also of the education of the understanding.[1]

This was written in 1854, when psychology was at the level represented by Dr Carpenter, who was satisfied that—

There *is* an entity wherein man's nobility essentially consists, which does not depend for its existence on any play of physical or vital forces, but which makes these forces subservient to its determination.[2]

That Dr Wallace accepts, with astounding credulity, the genuineness of the tricks of "spiritualist" charlatans of the Eusapio Paladino type ; that St George Mivart died, despite his treatment at the hands of his Church, a professed Catholic ; that Sir James Paget accepted, with never a doubt, the dogmas of orthodoxy ; and that Dr Carpenter was a Unitarian,—goes far to explain the attitude of each. But, surely, these opponents of the doctrine of continuity, by which Evolution stands or falls, had they made the effort, must have found it difficult to envisage the moment of supernatural intervention in the history of man when he passed from the mortal to the immortal ; when the "entity" which was not *of* him was injected *into* him.

[1] *Memoir*, by his Son, p. 175.   [2] *Mental Physiology*, p. 27.

There is an inevitable vagueness in the words of each writer; but it must be assumed that they all reject the old "preformation" theory of Leibnitz and Haller, and agree as to the importation of a separate "ens," or "being," into every man of woman born, whereby the individual becomes "a living soul." That being so, it is permissible to ask at what stage of gestation or of subsequent development the supernatural act of special creation, for that is what it comes to, was effected? It must be admitted that, prior to this, man must be at least potentially, if not, by reason of his slow develop-ment, actually, an animal of highly equipped intelligence. There is no need, in the common phrase, to "pause for a reply," because no reply is possible. A few words of Huxley's will, as usual, clear the atmosphere of verbal fog :—

No one who is cognisant of the facts of the case nowadays doubts that the roots of psychology lie in the physiology of the nervous system. What we call the operations of the mind are functions of the brain, and the materials of con-sciousness are products of cerebral activity. Cabanis may have made use of crude and misleading phraseology when he said that the brain secretes thought as the liver secretes bile ; but the conception which that much - abused phrase em-bodies is, nevertheless, far more consistent with fact than the popular notion that the mind is a metaphysical entity seated in the head, but as independent of the brain as a tele-graph operator is of his instrument.

It is hardly necessary to point out that the doctrine just laid down is what is commonly called materialism. But it is, nevertheless, true that the doctrine contains nothing inconsistent with the purest idealism. For as Hume remarks (as indeed Descartes had observed long before): "'Tis not our body we perceive when we regard our limbs and members, but certain impressions which enter by the senses ; so that the ascribing a real and corporeal existence to these impressions, or to their objects, is an act of the mind as difficult to explain as that [the external existence of objects] which we examine at present." Therefore, if we analyse the proposition that all mental phenomena are the effects or products of material phenomena, all that it means amounts to this : that whenever those states of consciousness which we call sensation, or emotion, or thought come into existence, complete investigation will show good reason for the belief that they are preceded by those other phenomena of consciousness to which we give the names of matter and motion. All material changes appear, in the long-run, to be modes of motion ; but our knowledge of motion is nothing but that of a change in the place and order of our sensations ; just as our knowledge of matter is restricted to those feelings of which we assume it to be the cause.[1]

Were it not, as Huxley says, that "the ignorance of the so-called educated classes is colossal," there might be need for apology in restatement of the fact that man is not descended from the ape. The relationship between them is lateral, not lineal, both being offshoots of the same stock, but each remaining, of course in very different degrees of development, isolated groups of mammals. The blood-relationship of the two has naturally prompted the question as to the missing link. A pertinent question, which has partial answer in the fact that all intermediate forms are, in virtue of their transitional character, the least likely to survive,

[1] *Coll. Essays*, vi. pp. 94, 95.

and in the further fact that the chances against the preservation of any remains of the progenitor of man and ape are as manifold as those against the preservation of any fossils of animals of correspondingly small size. Even in the period when rudely-fashioned stone tools and weapons of undoubted human origin abound, the occurrence of fragments of human skeletons is rare. In the section on " Fossil Remains of Man " in *Man's Place in Nature* Huxley discusses the value of the evidence supplied by skulls found in various bone-caverns of Western Europe, discoveries to which several important additions have been made since 1863. Comparing these with the skulls of the lowest savages extant, notably the Australian aborigines, he considered that we are not taken " appreciably nearer to that lower pithecoid form, by the modification of which man has, probably, become what he is." Where, then, he asks, " must we look for primeval Man ? Was the oldest *Homo sapiens* pliocene or miocene, or yet more ancient ? In still older strata do the fossilised bones of an Ape more anthropoid, or a Man more pithecoid, than any yet known, await the researches of some unborn palæontologist ? Time will show."

Time has not yet shown. But in 1892 Dr Eugéne Dubois found in the upper Pliocene beds at Trinil, on the banks of the river Bengavan, in Java, a calvaria or portion of skull, two molar teeth, and a thigh-bone, which he assumed belonged to an animal named by him *Pithecanthropus erectus*, or " upright ape - man."

The forehead was low and narrow, the inner surface of the skull bore impressions of convolutions, and M. Dubois estimated that the brain was about twice as large as that of the brain of the largest anthropoid. Although the shape of the thigh-bone warranted the inference that the creature walked erect, it also indicated adaptation to a tree-climbing habit absent in the human thigh-bone. Siam and Java may, in the upper Tertiary period, have been joined to the main-land; and these remains of the "upright ape-man" occur in a region where it is highly probable that man and ape became differentiated.

When Huxley published his book he had to meet the objection that the belief in the common origin of man and brute involved the brutalisation and degrada-tion of the former. But, he asks—

Is this really so? Could not a sensible child confute, by obvious arguments, the shallow rhetoricians who would force this conclusion upon us? Is it, indeed, true that the Poet, or the Philosopher, or the Artist, whose genius is the glory of his age, is degraded from his high estate by the un-doubted historical probability, not to say certainty, that he is the direct descendant of some naked and bestial savage, whose intelligence was just sufficient to make him a little more cunning than the Fox, and by so much more dan-gerous than the Tiger? Or is he bound to howl and grovel on all-fours because of the wholly unquestionable fact that he was once an Egg, which no ordinary power of dis-crimination could distinguish from that of a Dog? Or is the philanthropist or the saint to give up his endeavour to lead a noble life because the simplest study of man's nature reveals at its foundations all the selfish passions and fierce appetites of the merest quadruped? Is mother-love vile because a hen shows it, or fidelity base because dogs possess it?

The common-sense of the mass of mankind will answer these questions without a moment's hesitation. Healthy humanity, finding itself hard pressed to escape from real sin and degradation, will leave the brooding over speculative pollution to the cynics and the "righteous overmuch," who, disagreeing in everything else, unite in blind insensibility to the nobleness of this visible world, and in inability to appreciate the grandeur of the place Man occupies therein.

Nay more, thoughtful men, escaped from the blinding influences of traditional prejudice, will find in the lowly stock whence man has sprung, the best evidence of the splendour of his capacities; and will discern in his long progress through the Past a reasonable ground of faith in his attainment of a nobler Future.[1]

Several causes united to give man his pre-eminence and distinctive place in the "files of time." The slow acquirement of the erect position led to the flattening of the feet ; to projection of the heel as support ; and to the altered position of the skull with the added weight of brain which went on *pari passu* with new functions, the skull becoming nicely balanced on the spine, which became more curved, and, therefore, a better support. The bipedal position set free the arms from the work of locomotion, enabling man to use them as organs for grasping things, whereby their nature was ascertained, and for the manifold purposes which the struggle for life compelled. Interaction of brain and hand, together with increased modification of the thumb as

1 *Man's Place in Nature*, pp. 110, 111.

opposable, went on; while the gregarious instinct, more and more developed, bound the members together in ever enlarging groups, whose mutual dependence led to their permanence, and to the survival of the strongest.

To these purely natural factors is to be added the enormous part played by the evolution of articulate speech. "Much water has flowed under the bridges" since David Hartley, a pioneer-anthropologist of the eighteenth century, of whom Huxley had high appreciation, expressed the opinion that, owing to the shortness of the time which has elapsed since the Flood, both language and writing must have been given by direct miraculous agency.[1] Small blame to the philosophers of that time; but not to those who, in our own, would place the faculty of speech among the supernatural endowments of man. For modern physiology has not only demonstrated that the cortex, or layer of grey cellular substance, which covers the cerebrum, is the organ of the mind; it has localised the psychic centres to which the several sensory nerves telegraph their reports from the outer world, and it has also determined the place of the motor centre of articulate speech. In discussing the structural changes in the brain which have made possible the associated movement required for that "priceless gift," Professor D. J. Cunningham, in the address already referred to, shows by what slow processes of

---

[1] Hartley, *Prop.* lxxxiii., quoted by Leslie Stephen, *History of English Thought in the Eighteenth Century*, i. p. 193.

natural growth it must have been acquired. The more intelligent of the lower animals communicate with one another and express their feelings by various sounds, and the progenitors of man acted likewise. The actual germs of language existed in a few formless roots, most of these being natural sounds, whether in the tumbling of waters or the song of birds, and it is in the imitation of these sounds that the large number of words known as onomatopoetic, and the enormous number of words derived from them, have their rise. All sounds were supplemented by gestures and postures, which, among some races, still play a great part in communication. And it is to a physical and sensible source that our most abstract and metaphysical terms are traceable. For example, when we "apprehend" a thing, we "lay hold" of it; when we "apply" ourselves we bend "towards"; when we "transfer" we "carry"; to "concrete" is to combine particles together, while to "abstract" is to remove them; and few of us remember that in calling any one "supercilious" we mean, literally, that he raises his eyebrows. The choice and currency of this and that sound obviously lay in the aptness with which it conveyed the meaning in the mind of the speaker to that of the listener. Here we may use the terms of "natural selection" and say that the fittest for the purpose survived, and passed into the vocabulary, becoming the parent of a great group of words.

Without question, the acquisition of speech became a dominant factor in determining the high develop-

ment of the human brain.   To quote Professor Cunningham :—

The first word uttered expressive of an external object
marked a new era in the history of our early progenitors.
At this point the simian or brute-like stage in their develop-
mental career came to an end, and the human dynasty,
endowed with all its intellectual possibilities, began.   The
period in the evolution of man at which this important step
was taken was a vexed question, and one in the solution of
which we had little solid ground to go upon beyond the
material changes produced in the brain, and the consideration of the time that these might reasonably be supposed to
take in their development. . . . The structural characters
which distinguish the human brain in the region of the
speech-centre constitute one of the leading peculiarities of
the human cerebral cortex ; they are totally absent in the
brain of the anthropoid ape, and of the speechless micro-
cephalic idiot.   Further, it was significant that in certain
anthropoid brains a slight advance in the same direction
might occasionally be faintly traced, whilst in certain human
brains a distinct backward step is sometimes noticeable.
The path which had led to this special development was thus
in some measure delineated.   These structural additions to
the human brain were no recent acquisition by the stem-
form of man, but were the result of a slow evolutionary
growth, a growth which had been stimulated by the laborious
efforts of countless generations to arrive at the perfect co-
ordination of all the muscular factors which were called into
play in the production of articulate speech.[1]

"It goes without saying" that in his all-round
application of the doctrine of evolution Huxley came
to close quarters with those who demand the exclusion

[1] *Times*, September 14, 1901.

of the psychical nature of man from its operations. In one of the last papers that he wrote he contended, with rigorous logic, that "if man has come into existence by the same process of evolution as other animals; if his history, hitherto, is that of a gradual progress to a higher thought and a larger power over things; if that history is essentially natural, the frontiers of the new world, within which scientific method is supreme, will receive such a remarkable extension as to leave little but cloud-land for its rival." [1]

The discoveries of the astronomer since the time of Copernicus had compelled momentous changes in old conceptions of the relation of the earth to the other bodies of space; those of the geologists, from the time of Hutton and Lyell, had modified ideas concerning its age and the processes moulding its surface; and those of the palæontologists, from the time of Cuvier, had revolutionised theories of the origin of death as due to the original sin of Adam. A yet more profound revolution was set afoot when the rude tools and weapons of ancient river-gravels and bone-caverns brought their witness to man's high antiquity and primitive savagery, since therein was the further refutation of the doctrine of his fall on which the scheme of his redemption rests. To these witnesses were added those supplied by students of comparative mythology as to the origin of the Creation, Paradise, and other legends, evidencing these to be the

[1] *Nature*, November 1, 1894.

product of pre-scientific periods, when myths, gathering sanctity with age, became the unquestioned explanations of phenomena.

Hence, the old positions, one by one, have been abandoned on the advance of solid phalanxes of facts, until the defenders, strong in faith in its ultimate impregnability, have made their last stand within the citadel of Mansoul. But all in vain. The venerable walls, mounted with the old weapons of obscurantism, ignorance, and misrepresentation, have been stormed by the resistless forces of truth, and although the opening of the gates to the victor be delayed, his triumph is assured. But of this conflict—the Jehad of Science—in which Huxley was "gladiator-general" and inspirer, more anon.

Meanwhile, to return to his work as interpreter, it must be borne in mind that, hitherto, his exposition of the theory of evolution had been limited to the organic. Thus far he followed Darwin, the *Origin of Species* not being concerned with the evolution of the inorganic, nor with the problem of the origin of life, nor with the relation of the living to the not-living. As already noted, speculations on these high matters had their rise in Ionia five or six centuries before Christ, and, after an arrest of a thousand years, due to political and theological changes, had made a new start some three hundred years ago. But it was not until the last century was well advanced that any attempt to co-ordinate the several branches of knowledge into a harmonious theory of development was possible, and for the achievement of this the world is indebted to Mr Herbert Spencer, whose "Synthetic Philosophy," dealing with evolution as an all-inclusive process, begins with the condensation of vaporous stuff into cosmic systems, and ends with the development of human society. He explains all phenomena, from suns to souls, as the necessary results of the persistence of force under its forms of matter and motion, both indestructible, both ever changing, that which thus persists being "an unknown and unknowable" power, which we are obliged to recognise as without limit in space and without beginning or end in time. Thus, in endless rhythm, are the changes rung on Evolution and Dissolution from eternity to eternity. Huxley did "not very much care to speak of anything as 'unknowable,' and regrets that he made the mistake of wasting a capital 'U' upon it." [1] What he was sure about was that there were many things concerning which he knew nothing, and which, so far as he could see, were out of reach of human faculties.

Whether these things are knowable by any one else is exactly one of those matters which is beyond my knowledge, though I may have a tolerably strong opinion as to the probabilities of the case. Relatively to myself, I am quite sure that the region of uncertainty—the nebulous country in which words play the part of realities—is far more extensive than I could wish. [2]

But his indorsement of Mr Spencer's contention as to

[1] *Coll. Essays*, v. p. 311 ; and see NOTE, *infra*, p. 220.
[2] *Ib.*, p. 311.

the fundamental unity of the organic and the inorganic was emphatic. In an address to the International Medical Congress in 1881 he says:—

> In nature, nothing is at rest, nothing is amorphous ; the simplest particle of that which men in their blindness are pleased to call "brute matter" is a vast aggregate of molecular mechanisms performing complicated movements of immense rapidity, and sensitively adjusting themselves to every change in the surrounding world.
>
> And living matter differs from other matter in degree and not in kind ; the microcosm repeats the macrocosm ; and one chain of causation connects the nebulous original of suns and planetary systems with the protoplasmic foundation of life and organisation.[1]

Thirteen years earlier he had said the same thing on a Sunday evening in November to an Edinburgh audience. Like his wonderful discourse on "Animal Automatism," delivered before the British Association at Belfast, his Edinburgh "lay sermon" on "The Physical Basis of Life" was spoken without dependence on note or reference, and afterwards written out from memory for publication. Following on the demonstration of the identical constitution of protoplasm as the raw stuff which builds up the cell as the structural foundation of every living thing, Huxley showed that the protoplasm itself is built up of certain compounds, and that "a threefold unity—namely, a unity of power or faculty, a unity of form, and a unity of substantial composition — pervades the whole living world."

[1] *Coll. Essays*, iii. p. 371.

In whatever form protoplasm is manifest, whether, as in the very lowest plant or animal, without a nucleus, or, as in the higher organisms, nucleated, there are found four of the elementary substances, carbon, hydrogen, oxygen, and nitrogen, in very complex union. These non-living materials the plant, and the plant alone, by some mysterious alchemy, converts into a living thing, and upon this the animal sustains life. It is not easy to determine where the plant ends and where the animal begins, since some organisms exhibit the characters of both, but, broadly speaking, the fact abides that the animal depends on the vegetable. And, clearly, the vegetable depends, plus the energy of the sun, on the mineral. Each of the four elements of which protoplasm is made up is, by itself, ineffective to produce the organic ; united, they are stirred by complex movements of astounding rapidity which constitute the phenomena of life at its simplest ; life whose " hidden bond connects the flower which a girl wears in her hair with the blood which courses through her youthful veins," and the " brightly coloured lichen, which so nearly resembles a mere mineral incrustation of the bare rock on which it grows, with the painter, to whom it is instinct with beauty, and the botanist, whom it feeds with knowledge." [1]

The dependence of the highest upon the lowest living things, and, to a certain extent, the close relation between them, is too obvious to be questioned ;

[1] *Coll. Essays*, i. p. 131.

but so great is the reluctance to push things to conclusions involving collision with traditionally-received
ideas, that this admission does not affect the common
belief in a difference of kind, say, between the standing
corn and the man who reaps it for his daily bread.
Still stronger is the feeling that life itself, whether in
the weed or the philosopher, is an "entity" *in* matter,
but not *of* it; the view which, as has been seen, Dr
Alfred Russel Wallace and others hold concerning the
introduction of a spiritual faculty into man at some
stage of his development being extended, in the popular
mind, to the introduction of life on the globe as due to
the direct action of the Almighty. Huxley's assertion,
that "living matter differs from other matter in degree
and not in kind," is, therefore, a hard saying, and few
there be who accept it. It seems to shatter "the
mighty hopes that make us men." The theory that
man has descended, in an unbroken chain, like all the
other higher animals, from simple life-forms, offends his
"pride of life"; but the theory that there is no difference in kind between him and the dust on which he
treads excites his repugnance, and stirs him to revolt.
It was repellent enough to make him one with the tardy
snail and the immobile oyster, for the question of his
immortality seemed thereby involved with that of theirs;
but to make him one with the lifeless earth seemed the
very "superfluity of naughtiness," and the outcome of a
diabolical materialism.

Huxley knew that this cry would be raised when

he went to Edinburgh. And although, as will be seen, he made "a protest, from the philosophical side, against what is commonly called 'materialism,'" he found himself "generally credited with having invented 'protoplasm' in the interests of 'materialism.'"[1] But he proceeded to justify his words by the following comparison, the design of which was to show that the ultimate nature of matter is as fully a mystery as that of mind, and that the terms in which we speak of the one are equally applicable to the other.

Carbon, hydrogen, oxygen, and nitrogen, when brought together under certain conditions, give rise to the complex stuff, protoplasm, which manifests what is known as life. When two of these elements, oxygen and hydrogen, are mixed in a certain proportion, and an electric spark is passed through them, they disappear, and the result is water. In the one case we talk of a "vital force" having stirred the dead elements into living matter; but in the other case we do not talk of a something called "aquosity" having blended the two invisible gases into visible water. Is not the one process as mysterious as the other?

Does anybody quite comprehend the *modus operandi* of an electric spark, which traverses a mixture of oxygen and hydrogen?

What justification is there, then, for the assumption of the existence in the living matter of a something which has no representative or correlative in the not-living matter which

[1] *Lay Sermons*, Preface, p. vii.

I

gave rise to it? What better philosophical status has
"vitality" than "aquosity"? . . . If the phenomena exhibited by water are its properties, so are those presented
by protoplasm, living or dead, its properties. If the properties of water may be properly said to result from the
nature and disposition of its component molecules, I can find
no intelligible ground for refusing to say that the properties
of protoplasm result from the nature and disposition of its
molecules. . . .

It may seem a small thing to admit that the dull vital
actions of a fungus or a foraminifer are the properties of
their protoplasm, and are the direct results of the nature of
the matter of which they are composed. But if their protoplasm is essentially identical with, and most readily converted
into, that of any animal, I can discover no logical halting-
place between the admission that such is the case and the
further concession that all vital action may, with equal pro-
priety, be said to be the result of the molecular forces of the
protoplasm which displays it. And if so, it must be true, in
the same sense and to the same extent, that the thoughts
to which I am now giving utterance, and your thoughts
regarding them, are the expression of molecular changes
in that matter of life which is the source of our other vital
phenomena.[1]

The origin of life remains, and will doubtless remain,
an unsolved problem, if for no other reason than the
absolute effacement of the primitive forms, the fragility
of which is to be inferred from all that is known of the
lowest organisms. But the problem of the origin of
water, without which life could not have been, also
remains unsolved. The chemist can both decompose
and produce water; but, as Huxley asks, who can comprehend the *modus operandi* of the electric spark?

[1] *Coll. Essays*, i. pp. 152, 154.

Chemistry has also succeeded in manufacturing nearly two hundred organic compounds from dead matter; Professor Britschli has even produced a substance which simulates protoplasm,—but the *arcana vitæ* remains hidden. Nevertheless, noting what advances have been made in organic chemistry, in molecular physics, and in physiology, Huxley thinks that "it would be the height of presumption for any man to say that the conditions under which matter assumes the properties we call 'vital' may not be artificially brought together." The manifest intimate connection between vital and electrical phenomena is a further reason against dogmatism on the subject. And since the "scientific use of the imagination" has been the handmaid of progress, it is permissible to speculate, as does Huxley, on the possible mode of the beginning of life, whose "vital spark," once kindled, has, like the fire on the altar of Vesta, known no extinguishment.

To say that, in the admitted absence of evidence, I have any belief as to the mode in which the existing forms of life have originated, would be using words in a wrong sense. But expectation is permissible where belief is not ; and if it were given me to look beyond the abyss of geologically recorded time to the still more remote period when the earth was passing through physical and chemical conditions which it can no more see again than a man can recall his infancy, I should expect to be a witness of the evolution of living protoplasm from not-living matter. I should expect to see it appear under forms of great simplicity, endowed, like existing fungi, with the power of determining the formation of new protoplasm from such matters as ammonium carbonates, oxalates, and tartrates, alkaline and earthy phosphates, and water without the aid of light. That is the expectation to which analogical reasoning leads me ; but I beg you once more to recollect that I have no right to call my opinion anything but an act of philosophical faith.[1]

The success which has attended the search after fundamental likeness between the earth and its living, as well as not-living, contents, has followed all observation into the nature and constitution of the system of which the earth is one of the lesser members. While the conditions prevailing in the sun and planets make it certain that life, as we know it, cannot be present in them, the differences between them and our globe are only, using the term in its chemical sense, quantitative. They are made of the same stuff as the globe itself. So, broadly speaking, are the stars. The year 1859 is memorable in science, not only for the publication of the *Origin of Species*, but for the triumphant researches of Kirchhoff and Bunsen into the chemistry of the sun.

In 1802, one hundred and thirty years after Newton had refracted a sun-ray on a prism, and shown that light is made up of differently coloured rays, Wollaston, using a thin slit to admit the ray, observed that it was crossed by a few dark lines. In 1814 Fraunhofer succeeded, by means of yet finer apparatus, in detecting nearly six hundred of these lines. He, and following observers,· made shrewd guesses as to their meaning,

[1] *Coll. Essays*, viii, p. 256.

but another forty-five years passed before the riddle was read. The details of its solution are given in popular books on astronomy; and here it must suffice to say that the lines, which are now counted in their thousands, reveal the secret of the chemical constitution of the sun, and tell us that not only are iron, sodium, and some thirty other elements present in his atmosphere, the spectrum of iron alone numbering above two thousand lines, but that the raw materials of protoplasm, notably its most important constituent, carbon, are present also.[1] Kirchhoff's discovery was followed by Sir William Huggins's analysis of the light from stars and nebulæ, which proved that the former are made of like materials as the sun, himself a star of no high magnitude, and that the latter are gaseous, the vagrant comets having a spectrum which is a compound of carbon and hydrogen. The same astronomer also ingeniously discovered that a minute displacement of the lines of their spectra gave a key to the direction of the movements of the stars in space, while their colours indicate whether they are in the stages of youth, maturity, or decay.

It is a far cry from the apelike man to the nebula, and yet, in the foregoing rapid summary of cosmic processes, no warrant can be found for assumption of any break in causal relations. Nevertheless, when Huxley made the naked statement that there is no difference in kind between living and not-living matter; and when

[1] On the apparent absence of oxygen and nitrogen in the solar atmosphere, see my *Pioneers of Evolution*, p. 165.

Tyndall, decking the same in rhetorical garb, said that
"all our philosophy, all our poetry, all our science, all
our art—Plato, Shakespeare, Newton, and Raphael—
are potential in the fires of the sun,"[1] there can be
little wonder that charges of the kind made by the
Presbytery of Belfast, that they "ignored the existence
of God, and advocated pure and simple materialism,"
were levelled against them.

Huxley anticipated this; and in his Edinburgh
lecture, as later, more elaborately, in *Hume* and *Helps
to the Study of Berkeley*,[2] he deals with subjects which
bring us face to face with the ultimate problems of
philosophy. He was no tyro in these: from his early
boyhood, when, reading Sir William Hamilton, he
found only "cunning phrases for answers,"[3] his interest
in metaphysics had been deep and constant. He had
only scorn for the logomachies of the

"pure metaphysicians," who attempt to base the theory of
knowing upon supposed necessary and universal truths, and
assert that scientific observation is impossible unless such
truths are already known and implied, which to those who are
not " pure metaphysicians " seems very much as if one should
say that the fall of a stone cannot be observed unless the law
of gravitation is already in the mind of the observer.[4]

   The roots of every system of philosophy lie deep among
the facts of physiology. No one can doubt that the organs
and the functions of sensation are as much a part of the
province of the physiologist as are the organs and functions

---

[1] *Fragments of Science,* p. 453.
[2] These fill the sixth volume of *Collected Essays.*
[3] *Ante,* p. 3.   [4] *Coll. Essays,* vi. p. 62.

of motion or those of digestion ; and yet it is impossible to gain an acquaintance with even the rudiments of the physiology of sensation without being led straight to one of the most fundamental of all metaphysical problems. In fact, the sensory operations have been, from time immemorial, the battle-ground of philosophers.[1]

Wherefore, in the preface to the latest edition of *Hume*, he caustically advises those "who desire to discourse fluently and learnedly about philosophical questions to begin with the Ionians and to work steadily through to the latest speculative treatise"; while for those who "are animated by the much rarer desire for real knowledge," and who want to get a clear conception of the "deepest problems set before the intellect of man," he sees no need to travel outside "the limits of the English tongue." For this purpose "three authors will suffice, namely, Berkeley, Hume, and Hobbes." To which select company there may be added himself, with advice to master the sixth volume of *Collected Essays* and the papers on Descartes.[2]

A materialist, as commonly understood, holds that the universe is made-up of matter, of which all forms of activity, whether mechanical or spiritual, are products. The substance called matter is thus the substance of all things. This shallow view Huxley wholly repudiated, but not without protest against the vulgar idea of matter entertained by the majority of persons. In an appendix to a paper on the "Metaphysics of Sensation" he shows that what is loosely and ignorantly spoken of as dead or

[1] *Coll. Essays*, vi. p. 291.   [2] *Ib.*, i. pp. 166-250.

inert and altogether base—a notion due to Platonists
and to theologians, both of the East and West—throbs
with rhythmic movements of incredible rapidity, and is
charged with that element of true mystery wherein
wonder has its abiding source.

The handful of soil is a factory thronged with swarms of
busy workers ; the rusty nail is an aggregation of millions of
particles moving with inconceivable velocity in a dance of
infinite complexity, yet perfect measure ; harmonic with like
performances throughout the solar system.   If there is good
ground for any conclusion, there is such for the belief that
the substance of these particles has existed, and will exist,
that the energy which stirs them has persisted, and will
persist, without assignable limit, either in the past or in the
future. . . . Those who are thoroughly imbued with this view
of what is called "matter" find it a little difficult to understand why that which is termed "mind" should give itself
such airs of superiority over the twin sister, to whom, so far
as our planet is concerned, it might be hazardous to deny
the right of primogeniture.

Accepting the ordinary view of mind, it is a substance the
properties of which are states of consciousness, on the one
hand, and energy of the same order as that of the material
world (or else it would not be able to affect the latter) on the
other hand.   It is admitted that chance has no more place
in the world of mind than it has in that of matter.   Sensations, emotions, intellections are subject to an order as strict
and inviolable as that which obtains among material things.[1]

The question follows, " What can we know of what we
call matter or of what we call mind ? "   And the answer
is, So far as the ultimate nature of either is concerned,
nothing.   Our knowledge of both is inferential ; it is

[1] *Coll. Essays*, vi. p. 285.

limited to the impressions conveyed by the senses to the brain: in Huxley's words, "our knowledge is restricted to those feelings of which we assume external phenomena to be the cause."

The senses are the gateways of knowledge, and we assume that impulses vibrating from without enter these, and are conveyed by the nerves to the central nervous system—the seat of consciousness, or of knowledge of what goes on in the mind. We see, we smell, we hear, we taste, we touch; but the colour, the scent, the sound, the flavour, the hardness or softness, the warmth or cold-ness, are not in the things which we assume to be the cause of these sensations. They are in what is called "states of consciousness." How the passage is effected from the nerve-cells to consciousness we have no means of knowing. The thing is an insoluble mystery. The mutual dependence of what we call the body and what we call the mind is certain. We know nothing of mind apart from matter. We know that the brain is the organ of thought, and we cannot conceive of changes in the nerve-cells being produced by consciousness, so that the psychical seems wholly subordinate to the physical. Every feeling, every thought, is accompanied by molec-ular changes, and Huxley expressed the belief, which the "new psychology" may justify, that "we shall, sooner or later, arrive at a mechanical equivalent of consciousness, just as we have arrived at a mechanical equivalent of heat." [1] That marvellous faculty by which

[1] *Coll. Essays*, i. p. 191.

things are remembered appears to be due to molecular changes "which give rise to a state of consciousness, leaving a more or less persistent structural modification, through which the same molecular changes may be re-generated by other agencies than the cause which first produced them."[1]

Of course no sane person doubts the existence of an external world, or cosmos, built up, in Lord Kelvin's phrase, " of coarse-grained matter." Atoms are not, as Professor Rucker skilfully argued in his Presidential Address on the "Fundamental Concepts of Physics" to the British Association at Glasgow in 1901, "merely helps to puzzled mathematicians, but physical realities," probably made up of simpler parts, modifications of one *prima materia.* And in respect of force, the several modes of motion are explicable only on the assumption that particles of matter are being moved. Hence the atomic theory, despite recent attacks, holds the field.[2] Concerning these things, the common con-sciousness of mankind brings the same report, but the fact no less remains that we can only assume the exist-ence of beings with minds like our own. For they are a part of the phenomena whose ultimate nature, as was said above, we cannot know. There is "only one abstract certainty possible to man—namely, that at any given moment the feeling which he has exists. All

---

[1] *Coll. Essays,* i. p. 215.
[2] For Professor Rucker's Address, see *Times,* September 1, 1901.

other so-called certainties are beliefs of greater or less intensity."[1] The poet-astronomer of Naishapur stretches "lame hands" across the ages to the modern psychologist:—

> "We are no other than a moving row
> Of Magic Shadow-Shapes that come and go
> Round with the Sun-illumined Lantern held
> In Midnight by the Master of the Show."

But, as Huxley points out, although it is of small consequence whether we speak of the phenomena of matter in terms of spirit, or of those of spirit in terms of matter, since matter may be regarded as a form of thought, and thought may be regarded as a property of matter, there is every reason for using the materialistic terminology—

For it connects thought with the other phenomena of the universe, and suggests inquiry into the nature of those physical conditions, or concomitants of thought, which are more or less accessible to us, and a knowledge of which may help us to exercise the same kind of control over the world of thought as we already possess in respect of the material world : whereas the alternative, or spiritualistic, terminology is utterly barren, and leads to nothing but obscurity and confusion of ideas. . . . But the man of science who, forgetting the limits of philosophical inquiry, slides from these formulæ and symbols into what is commonly understood by materialism, seems to me to place himself on a level with the mathematician who should mistake the x's and y's with which he works his problems for real entities, and with this further disadvantage, as compared with the mathematician, that the blunders of the latter are of no practical consequence, while the errors of

---

[1] II. 262.

systematic materialism may paralyse the energies and destroy the beauty of a life.[1]

In his repudiation of the coarser materialistic views of the universe, and in his recognition of what insoluble mystery attends the connection between the thoughts of a man and the organ of those thoughts, Huxley was under no delusion that he had disarmed old prejudices, or secured any deserters from the orthodox camp. For, in place of conceding anything, he had only made clearer his hostility towards the supernatural explanations in which alone his opponents found rest and satisfaction. And seeing to what narrow dimensions the region once covered by those explanations had shrunk before the advance of the forces of natural knowledge, he pressed on to conquest of what remained.

[1] *Coll. Essays* i. pp. 164, 165.

IV.

THE CONTROVERSIALIST.

In a letter to his wife, written at Baden, in 1873, Huxley says :—

We are in the midst of a gigantic movement, greater than that which preceded and produced the Reformation, and really only the continuation of that movement. But there is nothing new in the ideas which lie at the bottom of the movement, nor is any reconcilement possible between free thought and traditional authority. One or other will have to succumb after a struggle of unknown duration, which will have as side issues vast political and social troubles. I have no more doubt that free thought will win in the long-run than I have that I sit here writing to you, or that this free thought will organise itself into a coherent system, embracing human life and the world as one harmonious whole. But this organisation will be the work of generations of men, and those who further it most will be those who teach men to rest in no lie, and to rest in no verbal delusions. I may be able to help a little in this direction—perhaps I may have helped already.[1]

Until his retirement, twelve years afterwards, that help was, perforce, rendered only fitfully ; but, once

[1] I. 397.

master of his time, Huxley said that whether it was long or short, he should devote it to the work outlined in the papers on the "Evolution of Theology."[1] There was to be no truce with "that ecclesiastical spirit, that clericalism, which is the deadly enemy of science." The battle had gone on, intermittently, for a quarter of a century. A fortnight after the famous duel with Wilberforce, when writing to Hooker about a proposed scientific quarterly, Huxley jocosely said that its tone would be "mildly episcopophagous,"[2] and in 1889 he asks Professor Ray Lankester if he sees "any chance of educating the white corpuscles of the human race to destroy the theological bacteria which are bred in parsons."[3] The author of *Lay Sermons*, let it be said, had the making of a preacher in him.   In the fragment of autobiography reprinted in the first volume of the *Collected Essays*, he tells how in early childhood he turned his pinafore wrong side forwards to represent a surplice, and held forth to his mother's kitchenmaids. And the impression of his homiletic gifts has sly reference in Bishop Thirlwall's *Letters to a Friend*,[4] when, speaking of the Metaphysical Society (founded in 1869), he says that "among the contributors to its proceedings have been Archbishop Huxley and Professor Manning."

Polemics, as Huxley said, "are always more or less an evil."   But the lukewarmness which lets error and corruption pursue their baneful course is a greater evil. And in the questions at issue between the exponents of

[1] *Coll. Essays*, iv. chap. viii.   [2] I. 210.   [3] II. 234.   [4] P. 317.

the doctrine of Evolution and the defenders of orthodoxy and privilege there was no place for indifference
or compromise. It was *guerre à outrance.* The
supremacy of clericalism involves the thraldom of the
mind, because its submission to an authority claiming
supernatural origin, and, therefore, one not to be
questioned, save at the soul's peril, was demanded. In
ordinary matters, the claimant to authority submits his
credentials, on the verification of which his claim is
admitted or rejected. And in matters of such high
import as the beliefs which rule a man's life, it would
seem that the same method should apply. Yet the
notion is widespread, even among intelligent persons,
that the credentials required in mundane things are
not to be demanded in what are deemed higher things.
The spiritual "powers that be"—bishops, priests, and
deacons—"are ordained of God," and the documents
on which their claims are based are exempt from
scrutiny. The prevalence of such a notion is explicable
only by the fact that the majority of people govern
their workaday lives on principles different from those
which operate in the creeds which they profess. They
rely, in lazy acquiescence, upon the assurances of the
official defenders of the faith that the "Church's one
foundation" remains unshaken. "Their faith," in the
words of Professor W. James, "is faith in some one
else's faith, and in the greatest matters this is most
the case." For inquiry involves effort, and there is
ease in travelling along the line of least resistance.

In opposition, wide as the poles asunder, to this,

the improver of natural knowledge absolutely refuses to acknowledge authority, as such. For him, scepticism is the highest of duties; blind faith the one unpardonable sin. And it cannot be otherwise, for every great advance in natural knowledge has involved the absolute rejection of authority, the cherishing of the keenest scepticism, the annihilation of the spirit of blind faith ; and the most ardent votary of science holds his firmest convictions, not because the men he most venerates hold them, not because their verity is testified by portents and wonders; but because his experience teaches him that whenever he chooses to bring these convictions into contact with their primary source, Nature—whenever he thinks fit to test them by appealing to experiment and to observation—Nature will confirm them. The man of science has learned to believe in justification, not by faith, but by verification.[1]

And it was because clericalism demanded acceptance of its claims in "blind faith" that Huxley would make no terms with it.

"I am very glad," he writes to a correspondent, "that you see the importance of doing battle with the clericals. I am astounded at the narrowness of view of many of our colleagues on this point! They shut their eyes to the obstacles which clericalism raises in every direction against scientific ways of thinking, which are even more important than scientific discoveries.

"I desire that the next generation may be less fettered by the gross and stupid superstitions of orthodoxy than mine has been."[2]

He observed that the conversion of a man into a "clerk in holy orders" was not attended with any addi-

[1] *Coll. Essays*, i. pp. 40, 41.   [2] II. 234.

tion to his intelligence. On the contrary, it leads to the cramping of his intellect, since at a fluent period of life, when he is on the threshold of its problems, he is required to stunt the further development of his mind by declaring that he accepts certain beliefs as final.[1] Nor does the clothing him with a shovel-hat, apron, and gaiters "in the smallest degree augment such title to respect as his opinions may intrinsically possess." [2] The emphasising of this in the case of bishops was the more necessary because the degree of importance with which the lay mind invests any statement by a cleric is regulated by his position in the Church. Huxley's "episcopophagy " took humorous form in the story of a country school lad who came near the boundary - line in an examination, one of his blunders consisting in putting the mitral valve, so-called from its resemblance to a mitre, on the right side of the heart instead of on the left side. "On appeal, Huxley let him through, observing, 'Poor little beggar, I never got them [the valves] correctly myself until I reflected that a bishop was never in the right.' " [3]

In opening the campaign, Huxley did not waste

---

[1] "If the clergy are bound down, and the laity unbound ; if the teacher may not seek the Truth, and the taught may ; if the Church puts the Bible in the hand of one as a living spirit and in the hand of the other as a dead letter—what is to come of it ? I *love* the Church of England. But what is to become of such a monstrous system, such a Godless lie as this ? " (To Professor Dawkins, 1862.) —*Letters* of (the then Rev.) John Richard Green, p. 110.

[2] *Coll. Essays*, i. p. 249 ; and see Morley's *Diderot*, ii. p. 50 (note). [3] II. 415.

powder and shot on that irreconcilable enemy of
knowledge and the liberty which is its fruit, the Roman
Catholic Church, "the one great spiritual organisation
which is able to resist, and must, as a matter of life and
death, resist the progress of science and modern civilisation."[1] He divided the clergy of the Established Church
into three sections : "an immense body who are ignorant,
and speak out ; a small proportion who know and are
silent ; and a minute minority who know and speak according to their knowledge." Only with the last-named
had he anything in common ; but his intellectual honesty
caused him to sympathise less with the "half-and-half
sentimental school," represented by divines of the type
of Dean Farrar, than "with thoroughgoing orthodoxy,"
as represented by the late Mr Spurgeon. Of one and
all of them it may be said that his thoughts were not
their thoughts, nor his ways their ways. He dealt with
facts ; they played with phrases. They acted as if "the
analysis of terms is the right way of knowledge, and
mistook the multiplication of propositions for the discovery of fresh truth."[2] And he thought them lacking
in straightforwardness. His conversation was "Yea,
yea," or "Nay, nay" ; theirs was evasive, or qualifying,
when a direct question was put to them. To him they
seemed to confuse much and to explain nothing. And
he felt that if men of science have not lightened our
darkness concerning many things, theologians have

[1] *Coll. Essays*, iii. p. 120.
[2] *Rousseau*, by John Morley, ii. p. 338.

only deepened it. To mix with them was to inhale a relaxing air wherein the fibres of veracity were loosened.

Some time before his death, the decay of dogmatic theology, which a changed intellectual atmosphere had brought about, was followed by a revival of sacerdotalism, the force of which has increased rather than abated. The result is a general materialising of "aids to faith." Churches and services are more ornate; the sensuous stimuli of music, incense, and colour are brought into play; greater stress is laid on the importance of baptismal and other sacramental rites, with the consequent aggrandisement of the sacerdotalist as their divinely authorised administrator. The emotions have unwholesome excitation; the reason is drugged. A sermon—if it be not a sleeping-draught—makes appeal to the intellect; it may convert, or it may fail to convince. But a rite requires unquestioning acceptance of its supernatural obligation and nature as the condition of its efficacy. To partake in it demands no mental effort. This thaumaturgy in religion has its correlatives in the pseudo-mysticism of the present day, as in the spurious remedies of "Christian Science" for diseases; in the trickeries of spiritualism, whose phenomena, were they true, would, as Huxley said, "furnish an additional argument against suicide";[1] in the charlatanry of palmistry, astrology, and other quackeries, evidencing how superficial are the changes in human nature. "So

[1] I. 420; and see *Coll. Essays*, v. pp. 341, 342.

little trouble," says Thucydides, " do men take in search
after truth ; so readily do they accept whatever comes
first to hand." [1]

Huxley was well equipped in historical knowledge.
When Dr St George Mivart cited Suarez and other
schoolmen in his criticisms on the *Origin of Species*, he
found his match in Huxley.   The outlines of the course
of events following the death of Jesus, which he gives in
his essays on the " Evolution of Theology," show that he
knew ecclesiastical history better than many ecclesiastics
themselves, for these too often know it only in the
idealised or partisan forms presented by orthodox
historians.   No thoughtful student of the past, with all
its cross-currents and complexities, will make the shame-
ful story of religious wars and persecutions an occasion
of reproach against the Churches of to-day.   Humanity
has a terrible indictment against theology, but the charge
cannot be laid at the door of our contemporaries.   Nevertheless, in the degree that the Church has not purged
herself of the old Adam of the anti-progressive spirit,
she stands condemned before the modern world, and
with no such plea as antiquity might offer.   Her condemnation is complete.   Taking history no farther back
than the last century, it will be found that there was not
a movement, political, social, or intellectual, having as
its aim the bettering of the condition of the people,
which she did not oppose tooth and nail.   She lifted no
voice against the barbaric criminal code under which.

[1] I. 20 (Jowett's trans.)

well within the nineteenth century, two hundred offences were punishable with death ; [1] her bishops opposed the measures for the abolition of theological tests for public offices, for the removal of disabilities on Roman Catholics, Jews, and Dissenters ; in the abolition of slavery in British possessions, and in the reform of the incredibly horrible state of prisons, and of the inhuman treatment of lunatics in this kingdom, she took no initiative; she fought against unsectarian elementary education ; she still wages bitter war to enforce the teaching of her dis-credited dogmas ; and, to her even greater shame, fans and fosters the spirit of militarism in temples on whose walls are inscribed, "On earth peace, and goodwill towards men." And, withal, trading on the ignorance of the multitude, her ministers have the audacity to claim credit for the removal of unjust and brutal measures from the statute-book of the realm, and for the general spread of humanitarianism; whereas it is solely to the development of sympathy born of know-ledge that these are due. The Church has tardily followed where these have led. For these reasons, written clear on the page of history, Huxley called the "ecclesiastical spirit the deadly enemy of science."

But for the confusion which men make between the

---

[1] OLD BAILEY.—William Keep, a lad of fourteen years of age, was indicted for stealing a Bank of England note out of a letter which had come into his possession in consequence of his having been employed in the General Post Office as a sorter of letters. . . . The jury found the prisoner—*Guilty—Death.—Times*, Nov. 1, 1801. The death-sentences were sometimes commuted.

letter and the spirit it should be needless to say that
Huxley had no quarrel—who can have?—with religion,
defining this as "a consciousness of the limitations of
man and a sense of an open secret which is impene-
trable,"[1] and as "the reverence and love for an ethical
ideal, and the desire to realise that ideal in life which
every man ought to feel."[2] The ideal will be low or
high according to the standard reached by a community,
but, whatever that standard may be, it represents the
attitude towards unseen or envisaged powers which
affect men deeply and constantly. No religion, however repellent it may be to refined natures, has taken
root which did not adjust itself to, and answer, some
need of the human heart. And the measure of our
knowledge of the various faiths of mankind will be the
measure of our sympathy. What quarrel the evolutionist may have is with the letter of theology, "which
killeth," not with the spirit of religion, which "giveth
life." As Huxley says —

The antagonism between science and religion, about
which we hear so much, appears to me to be purely factiti-
ous—fabricated, on the one hand, by short-sighted religious
people who confound a certain branch of science, theology,
with religion ; and, on the other, by equally short-sighted
scientific people who forget that science takes for its province
only that which is susceptible of clear intellectual compre-
hension. . . . The antagonism of science is to the heathen
survivals and the bad philosophy under which religion
herself is often wellnigh crushed. And I trust that this

---

[1] *Coll. Essays*, i. p. 33.   [2] *Ib.*, v. p. 250.

antagonism will never cease ; but that, to the end of time, true science will continue to fulfil one of her most beneficent functions, that of relieving men from the burden of false science, which is imposed upon them in the name of Religion.[1]

Superfluous to add, therefore, that Huxley was no iconoclast : no man who is imbued with the spirit of the doctrine of evolution, which links us to the past as its products and finds a warrant for all that yet has been, can be that. Regulation, not suppression, of human nature, was his aim. He was as anxious as any defender of the faith can be that religion should " bring forth the peaceable fruits of righteousness "; his care was to afford it free play by the removal of the accretions which make it unlovely and a reproach before the world. In an address delivered as far back as 1871, he said that he could

conceive the existence of an Established Church which should be a blessing to the community. A Church in which, week by week, services should be devoted, not to the itera- tion of abstract propositions in theology, but to the setting before men's minds of an ideal of true, just, and pure living ; a place in which those who are weary of the burden of daily cares should find a moment's rest in the contemplation of the higher life which is possible for all, though attained by so few ; a place in which the man of strife and of business should have time to think how small, after all, are the rewards he covets compared with peace and charity. Depend upon it, if such a Church existed, no one would seek to disestablish it.[2]

---

[1] *Coll. Essays*, iv. pp. 160, 163.   [2] *Ib.*, i. p. 284.

And he not only looked with no favour upon criticism
that is wholly destructive ; he demurred, " both as a
matter of principle and one of policy, to a great deal of
what appears as ' free thought' literature."

Heterodox ribaldry disgusts me, I confess, rather more
than orthodox fanaticism.   It is at once so easy ; so stupid ;
such a complete anachronism in England, and so thoroughly
calculated to disgust and repel the very thoughtful and
serious people whom it ought to be the great aim to attract.
Old Noll knew what he was about when he said that it was
of no use to try to fight the gentlemen of England with
tapsters and serving-men.   It is quite as hopeless to fight
Christianity with scurrility.   We want a regiment of
Ironsides.[1]

The mode of attack thus rightly censured is wellnigh obsolete.   The old fatuous alternatives, which presented Jesus as a divine being or an impostor, and the
Bible as an inspired book or a forgery, rarely enter into
modern methods of controversy.   The age may not be
very earnest, but it is not flippant, in these matters.
Beliefs are no longer only attacked, they are explained.
Religions are no longer treated as wholly true or as
wholly false, as the inventions of designing priests or
as of supernatural origin ; but as the product of man's
crude speculations concerning himself and his surroundings, and of his spiritual needs, no matter in what repul-
sive form these are satisfied.   And a survey shows how
each one, with its outcome in creed and ritual, falls into
line with the processes of evolution : how, like organ-

[1] II. 321.

isms, all spring from common elements; how, like these,
they bear within themselves the traces of their stages of
development; how natural selection acts upon them,
their survival depending on their power of adaptation,
and how, this failing, they perish and become fossilised
in the strata of obsolete creeds.

Beyond the general remark that religion arises, "like
all other kinds of knowledge, out of the action and
interaction of man's mind with that which is not in
man's mind, and takes the intellectual coverings of
Fetichism or Polytheism ; of Theism or Atheism, of
Superstition or Rationalism,"[1] Huxley refrained from
speculations as to the particular primary impulses which
gave this or that shape to it. All such speculations—
and history, both past and present, has seen many of
them—are foredoomed to failure, because the "Naturall
seed of *Religion*," as Hobbes calls it,[2] is the product of
roots that lie too deep down for discovery. They are
intertwined with man's psychical development ; they are
fed from the same sources whence arise the psychical
faculties of animals ; and as the student of comparative
mythology and comparative theology must take counsel
with the anthropologist and folk-lorist, so must all of
them take counsel with the comparative psychologist
and the comparative physiologist.

In such spirit, then, Huxley advanced to an examination of the "venerable record of ancient life, miscalled

[1] *Coll. Essays,* i. p. 138.
[2] *Leviathan :* "Of Man," ch. xii. pt. i.

a book,"[1] on which clericalism rests its claims and its creeds. A quarter of a century earlier there had been talk about prosecuting Jowett for the heretical article in *Essays and Reviews* wherein he laid down what seemed the irreverent canon, "Interpret the Scripture like any other book."[2] It would be difficult to say in what other way the Bible could be interpreted, and, since 1860, the comparative method, which has yielded valuable results in all departments of research, has been applied unchallenged to the sacred text:—

From my present point of view [said Huxley, in the opening pages of his essays on the "Evolution of Theology"], theology is regarded as a natural product of the operations of the human mind, under the conditions of its existence, just as any other branch of science, or the arts of architecture, or music, or painting, are such products. Like them, theology has a history. Like them also, it is to be met with in certain simple and rudimentary forms; and these can be connected by a multitude of gradations, which exist, or have existed, among people of various ages and races, with the most highly developed theologies of past and present times.

We are all likely to be more familiar with the theological history of the Israelites than with that of any other nation. We may therefore fitly make it the first object of our studies; and it will be convenient to commence with that period which lies between the invasion of Canaan and the early days of the monarchy, and answers to the eleventh and twelfth centuries B.C., or thereabouts. The evidence on which any conclusion as to the nature of Israelitic theology in those days must be based is wholly contained in the Hebrew

[1] *Coll. Essays,* iv. p. 289. [2] P. 377 (1861 edition).

Scriptures—an agglomeration of documents which certainly belong to very different ages, but of the exact dates and authorship of any one of which (except perhaps a few of the prophetical writings) there is no evidence, either internal or external, so far as I can discover, of such a nature as to justify more than a confession of ignorance, or, at most, an approximate conclusion. In these we have the stratified deposits (often confused, and even with their natural order inverted) left by the stream of the intellectual and moral life of Israel during many centuries. And, embedded in these strata, there are numerous remains of forms of thought which once lived, and which, though often unfortunately mere fragments, are of priceless value to the anthropologist. Our task is to rescue these from their relatively unimportant surroundings, and by careful comparison with existing forms of theology to make the dead world which they record live again. In other words, our problem is palæontological, and the method pursued must be the same that is employed in dealing with other fossil remains.[1]

From these rich deposits of ancient life-forms Huxley chose that which occurs in the twenty-eighth chapter of the first book of Samuel, and which tells the story of Saul's visit to the witch of Endor.

On the eve of a decisive battle between the Israelites and the Philistines, Saul, in despair because Jahveh had "answered him not, neither by dreams, nor by Urim, nor by prophets," sought counsel (despite his having banished wizards and their kin) of a woman "that had a familiar spirit," literally, "a woman mistress of *Ob*," which word means primitively a leather bottle, such as a wine-skin, and is applied alike to the necromancer and to the spirit evoked. It may be compared with the sacred snake-

[1] *Coll. Essays*, iv. pp. 288, 289.

skin bags or the magic drums which form part of the apparatus of the Red Indian medicine-men or sorcerers, the use of Ob being probably suggested "by the likeness of the hollow sound emitted by a half-empty skin when struck to the sepulchral tones in which the oracles of the evoked spirits were uttered by the medium." [1] Disguising himself, Saul sought the woman, who, at his request, called up the prophet Samuel from Sheol, the under-world. The apparition is visible to her, but invisible to the king (who had thrown off his disguise), to whose inquiry she replies, "I see Elohim (god or gods) coming up out of the earth." A conversation, through the woman as medium, follows between Saul and Samuel, who, reproaching the king for disquieting him, says, "Jahveh will deliver Israel also with thee into the hands of the Philistines, and to-morrow shalt thou and thy sons be with me" (*i.e.*, in Sheol).

The story throws a flood of light upon ancient Israelitic belief in necromancy and other forms of magic, and in the abode of the dead. This last had nothing in common with the elaborate conception of a future state of rewards and punishments which was incorporated into Hebrew eschatology during the Captivity. The belief in Sheol may be equated with that of the Greek belief in Hades, both these being survivals of barbaric ideas about the fate of the departed. "The small and great are there, and the servant is free from

---

[1] *Coll. Essays*, iv. p. 295. For various meanings of *Ob* see Art. "Divination" in *Encyclopædia Biblica*.

his master." The ancient Israelites thought that a man consists of body and soul, and that after death the soul continued to exist as a ghost in the under-world, whence it could be summoned by the art of the necromancer, retaining, on its appearance, some shadowy outline in form and feature by which it could be identified. As for Elohim, a term translated "god" (in contrast to Jahveh or Jehovah, translated "Lord"), that word, as was seen above, is applied to ghosts, and also to various grades of gods. Its use by the woman is of importance, as showing that the ghost had become in some degree deified, a process of apotheosis which marks the beginnings of ancestor-worship. The existence of this widespread cult among the Israelites is evidenced by the rude human images known as Teraphim. The reference to Urim shows the prevalence of divination. The Urim and Thummim appear to have been lots which were carried by the high priest in the pocket of his "breastplate," worn on the ephod. Besides these, there are evidences of other modes of ascertaining the will of heaven, as by rods,[1] pointless arrows,[2] and dreams,[3] while the important part played by sacrifices, usually burnt-offerings, in old Israelitic ritual, is too well known to need more than allusion here.

The theological system thus outlined offers to the anthropologist no feature which is devoid of a parallel in the known theologies of other races of mankind, even of those

---

[1] Hosea iv. 12.　　　　　　[2] Ezekiel xxi. 23.
[3] Genesis xx. 3, xxxi. 24 ; Judges vii. 13, &c.

who inhabit parts of the world most remote from Palestine. And the foundation of the whole, the ghost-theory, is exactly that theological speculation which is the most widely spread of all, and the most deeply rooted among uncivilised men.[1]

There is nothing new in the foregoing to readers of Kuenen's great work on the *Religion of Israel*, nor to those who have compared the archaic elements in the Bible with the details of belief and ritual among the lower races given in books of the type of Tylor's *Primitive Culture* and Frazer's *Golden Bough*. But, apart from the need of restating the obvious, Huxley's purpose and skill were shown in his focussing one or more salient features of the old Israelitic theology for comparison with active beliefs among lower races of whom he knew something at first hand, or concerning whom he had cogent testimony. For the first of these he drew on his Rattlesnake experiences. In December 1848 that vessel was anchored off Mount Ernest, an island in Torres Straits. Huxley and a shipmate, whom he calls B., went ashore, and in course of time became intimate with an old native named Paouda. The old man took to B. because he believed him to be his father-in-law.

His grounds for that singular conviction were very remarkable. We had made a long stay at Cape York hard by: and in accordance with a theory which is widely spread among the Australians, that white men are the incarnated spirits of black men, B. was held to be the ghost of a certain Mount Ernest native, one Antarki, who had lately died, on the ground of some real or fancied

---

[1] *Coll. Essays*, iv. p. 317.

resemblance to the latter.   Now Paouda had taken to wife
a daughter of Antarki's, named Domani, and as soon as
B. informed him that he was the ghost of Antarki, Paouda
at once admitted the relationship and acted upon it.   For,
as all the women on the island had hidden away in fear of
the ship, and we were anxious to see what they were like,
B. pleaded pathetically with Paouda that it would be very
unkind not to let him see his daughter and grandchildren.
After a good deal of hesitation and the exaction of pledges
of deep secrecy, Paouda consented to take B., and myself
as B.'s friend, to see Domani and the three daughters,
by whom B. was received quite as one of the family, while I
was courteously welcomed on his account.   This scene made
an impression upon me which is not yet effaced.   It left no
question on my mind of the sincerity of the strange ghost-
theory of these savages, and of the influence which their
belief has on their practical life.[1]

For the second, Huxley cites Mariner's *Account of the
Natives of the Tonga Islands in the South Pacific Ocean*,
published in 1816.   When he was quite a youth William
Mariner joined the Port-au-Prince, a private ship of war
commissioned to cruise for prizes in certain latitudes,
and, failing success in that, to search for whales.[2]   Her
fate was to be boarded, plundered, and destroyed by the
natives of Lafooga, one of the Tonga islands, where
Mariner, to whom Finow, the chief, had taken a fancy,
spent four years before making his escape.   He learned
the language and lived the life of the islanders, familiar-
ising himself with their beliefs and customs.   Concerning
their theology, he says—

The human soul, after its separation from the body, is

---

[1] *Coll. Essays*, iv. pp. 317, 318.   [2] Introd. to *Mariner*, i. p. xxv,

termed a *hotooa* (a god or spirit; hotooa is the same as the
better-known *atua*), and is believed to exist in the shape of
the body; to have the same propensities as during life, but
to be corrected by a more enlightened understanding, by
which it readily distinguishes good from evil, truth from
falsehood, right from wrong; having the same attributes as
the original gods, but in a minor degree, and having its
dwelling for ever in the happy regions of Bolotoo, holding
the same rank in regard to other souls as during this life:
it has, however, the power of returning to Tonga to inspire priests, relations, or others, or to appear in dreams to
those it wishes to admonish; and sometimes to the external
eye in the form of a ghost or apparition; but this power
of reappearance at Tonga particularly belongs to the souls
of chiefs than of matabooles (a kind of "clients" in the
Roman sense, as Huxley explains in a footnote).[1]

The "atuas" include gods good and evil, home and
foreign, as well as the souls of men, so that they "are
exactly equivalent" to the "Elohim" of the old
Israelites, while the description of the incidents attending the "inquiry of" an atua, as the paroxysm and
excitation of the priest, correspond "with the manifesta-
tions of abnormal mental states among ourselves, and
furnish a most instructive commentary upon the story
of the witch of Endor." Bolotoo answers to Sheol;
among the several hundred gods recognised by "the
Tongan theologians" one was greater than all, as among
the Israelites Jahveh was "god of gods." And both in
Palestine and the Pacific Ocean the anger of the deities
was believed to be manifest as strongly in the case of

[1] *Coll. Essays*, iv. p. 323; and *Mariner*, ii. p. 99 ff. (1827
edition).

neglect of ritual as for offences against the moral law. The result of these and other comparisons noted in the "Evolution of Theology" is to show how little is left to choose between them.

One may read from the beginning of the book of Judges to the end of the books of Samuel without discovering that the old Israelites had a moral standard which differs, in any essential respect (except perhaps in regard to the chastity of unmarried women) from that of the Tongans. Gideon, Jephthah, Samson, and David are strong-handed men, some of whom are not outdone by any Polynesian chieftain in the matter of murder and treachery. . . . But it is surely needless to carry the comparison further. Out of the abundant evidence at command I think that sufficient has been produced to furnish ample grounds for the belief that the old Israelites of the time of Samuel entertained theological conceptions which were on a level with those current among the more civilised of the Polynesian islanders, though their ethical code may possibly, in some respects, have been more advanced.[1]

Therefore, to whatever high spiritual altitudes the Israelites attained, and however distinctive may have been their genius for religion,—a genius which shaped their traditions, whether native or borrowed, in accordance with their belief in their special mission as instruments and witnesses of Jehovah among mankind, and which inspired their prophets to utterances unsurpassed in grandeur of expression and in loftiness of moral tone, —the documents of their religion evidence that they passed through stages of development corresponding to those of other races; stages of crude and coarse con-

[1] *Coll. Essays*, iv. pp. 340, 345.

ceptions of the gods, attended by a bloody ritual and a low morality.

While Huxley was busy over this subject, there appeared the article by Mr Gladstone, to the invigorating effects of which reference was made on page 50. In his notice of M. Reville's book Mr Gladstone took exception to the statement that while the Creation story and other narratives in the Pentateuch "possess a value of the highest order, they are not to be regarded as other than a venerable fragment, well deserving attention, of the great genesis of mankind." This was reducing them to the level of ordinary secular history, and hence Mr Gladstone sought to prove that, instead of "merely a lofty poem or a skilfully constructed narrative," we have, in the Hebrew cosmogony and all that follows it, "a revelation of truth from God," and the "great foundation-chapter of the entire Scriptures, New as well as Old." After defending the astounding theory of the creation of something out of nothing, he contended that the fourfold order of the appearance of living things set forth in the Hebrew cosmogony is confirmed by "natural science." He cited a few antiquated authorities, the greatest among these being Cuvier. But, as Huxley pointed out—

Cuvier has been dead more than half a century; and the palæontology of our day is related to that of his very much as the geography of the sixteenth century is related to that of the fourteenth. Since 1832, when Cuvier died, not only a new world but new worlds of ancient life have been discovered, and those who have most faithfully carried on the

work of the chief founder of palæontology have done most
to invalidate the essentially negative grounds of his speculative adherence to tradition. If Mr Gladstone's latest
information on these matters is derived from the famous
discourse prefixed to the "Ossemens Fossiles" I can understand the position he has taken up ; if he has ever opened
a respectable modern manual of palæontology or geology, I
cannot. For the facts which demolish his whole argument
are of the commonest notoriety.[1]

Concerning the controversy, "It was not," Sir Mount-
stuart Grant-Duff said, "so much a battle as a mas-
sacre." Nevertheless, after annihilation, as it seemed to
the onlooker, by Huxley's intellectual dynamite, Mr
Gladstone reappeared, as if never disturbed therefrom,
on the *Impregnable Rock of Holy Scripture*, as he called
it. In that book he reaffirmed, in ingenious variation of
phrase, all that Huxley had disproved concerning the succession of life-forms, and, passing from the organic to the
inorganic, contended that "the nebular theory supplies
a new and remarkable establishment of accord between
natural science on the one hand (so far as its reasoning
has proceeded) and the Book of Genesis on the other." [2]
Mr Gladstone had no sympathy with the invertebrate theologians who would transfer Christianity from a historical
to a psychological base. "We are," he says, "professors
of a religion which rests not so much on abstract principles as on matters of fact, inseparable from the revela-

[1] *Coll. Essays*, iv. p. 144.
[2] *Impregnable Rock of Holy Scripture*, chap. vi., "On Recent
Corroborations of Scripture from the Regions of History and
Natural Science."

tion itself." Such physical facts are the Creation, the
Incarnation, the Resurrection.[1] As to the validity of
these, no doubt had ever possessed him. He writes as
a man of apparently open mind, but throughout life
every avenue had been shut against the admission of
anything telling against preconceptions which were
theological to the core. Mr George Russell wrote a
pamphlet on "Mr Gladstone's Religious Development."
It should have been issued in blank, for Mr Gladstone
never had any such development. He was in the
nineties what he was in the thirties, save that with ad-
vancing years he attached greater importance to ritual
observances. One evidence of this is his resignation of
membership of the Folklore Society in 1896, when the
Presidential Address of that year, dealing with the significance of that portion of Dr Frazer's *Golden Bough*
which treats of the large body of barbaric rites connected with "eating the god," pointed out the relation
of these to the sacrament. His whilom colleague and
brother-Churchman, Lord Selborne, said of him that "he
was too readily influenced by opinions which fell in with
his own wishes or feelings, and by the men who held
them, and was impatient of the dry light of facts when
facts told the other way. He could see into millstones
farther than other men, and, on the other hand, he had
a wonderful power of not seeing what he did not like."[2]

[1] *Impregnable Rock of Holy Scripture*, chap. ii., "The Creation
Story."

[2] *Memorials: Personal and Political*, 1865-1895.

The facts of natural science were accepted by him only in so far as they were shown to be in accord with the statements of Scripture; and, as they could not be ignored, the instruments of ambiguity and evasiveness, which perform their disingenuous work in political controversy, were employed to bring these facts into seeming harmony with revelation. Hence the serious limitations to which Mr John Morley bore witness when unveiling a statue to Mr Gladstone at Manchester in October last year.

Something [he says] was left out in the wide circle of his interests ; natural science in all its speculations and extensions and increase of scientific truth, extension of scientific methods—all that no doubt constitute the central activities, the intellectual activities of England and Europe during the last forty years of his life—to all that he was not entirely open.[1]

I remember once going with him one Sunday afternoon to pay a visit to Mr Darwin. It was in the seventies. As I came away I felt that no impression had reached him that that intellectual, modest, single-minded lover of truth—that searcher of the secrets of nature—was one who from his Kentish hill-top was shaking the world. But the omission of scientific interest was made up for. The thought with which he rose in the morning and went to rest at night was of the universe as a sublime moral theatre, on which the Omnipotent Dramaturgist used kingdoms and rulers, laws and policies, to exhibit a sovereign purpose for good, to light up what I may call the prose of politics with a ray from the Diviner Mind, and exalted his ephemeral discourses in a sort of visible relation to the counsels of all time.

---

[1] "Of natural science he was strangely ignorant."—Mr Bryce, "On some Traits of Mr Gladstone," *Fortnightly Review*, January 1902, p. 13.

While Mr Gladstone, as wellnigh the last of the old school of reconcilers, was renewing the hopeless attempt to harmonise, by verbal legerdemain, Genesis and Geology, contending, for example, that the six days meant " six chapters in the history of the creation," liberal theologians were surrendering belief in the historical character of the so - called " Mosaic " writings.

" I cannot deny," said Canon Bonney, speaking at the Church Congress held in 1895 at Norwich, " that the increase of scientific knowledge has deprived parts of the earlier books of the Bible of the historical value which was generally attrib-uted to them by our forefathers. The story of the creation in Genesis, unless we play fast and loose either with words or with science, cannot be brought into harmony with what we have learned from geology. Its ethnological statements are imperfect, if not sometimes inaccurate. The stories of the flood and of the Tower of Babel are incredible in their present form. Some historical elements may underlie many of the traditions in the first eleven chapters of that book, but this we cannot hope to recover."

In his essay on " Hebrew Authority " in *Authority and Archæology*, Dr Driver, Regius Professor of Hebrew in the University of Oxford, and sitting, therefore, in the chair of Pusey, says that

the general result of the archæological and anthropological researches of the past half-century has been to take the Hebrews out of the isolated position which, as a nation, they seemed previously to hold, and to demonstrate their affinities with, and often their dependence upon, the civilisations by which they were surrounded. . . . The civilisation which, in spite of the long residence of the Israelites in Egypt, left its

mark, however, most distinctly upon the culture and literature of the Hebrews was that of Babylonia. It was in the
East that the Hebrew traditions placed both the cradle of
humanity and the more immediate home of their own ancestors ; and it was Babylonia which, as we now know,
exerted during many centuries an influence, once unsuspected, over Palestine itself. . . . Thus the beliefs (of the
Hebrews) about the origin and early history of the world,
their social usages, their code of civil and criminal law,
their religious institutions, can no longer be viewed, as was
once possible, as differing in kind from those of other nations,
and determined in every feature by a direct revelation from
Heaven ; all, it is now known, have substantial analogies
among other peoples, the distinctive character which they
exhibit among the Hebrews consisting in the spirit with
which they are infused, and the higher principles of which
they are made the exponent. Their literature, moreover,
it is now apparent, was not exempt from the conditions to
which the literature of other nations was subject ; it embraces,
for instance, narratives relating to what we should term the
prehistoric age, similar in character and scope to those oc-
curring in the literature of other countries. There are many
representations and statements in the Old Testament which
only appear in their proper perspective when viewed in the
light thrown upon them by archæology. And in some cases
it is not possible to resist the conclusion that they must be
interpreted in a different sense from that in which past
generations have commonly understood them.[1]

The Creation-story, with which the book of Genesis
opens, can no longer be regarded " as possessing any
value as a scientific exposition of the past history of the
earth." There is now no question whatever that it was
derived from the Babylonian epic, the grotesque poly-

[1] Pp. 7, 8.

theism of which is, in the Hebrew variant, superseded
by "a severe and dignified monotheism." The Sabbath
is, in all probability, an institution ultimately of Babylonian origin, not then as a rest-day for man, but "a day
when the gods rested from their anger." Among the
Hebrews it was made subservient to human needs and
religious purposes; but "its sanctity is explained un-
historically, and ante-dated."

Instead of the Sabbath, closing the week, being sacred,
because God rested upon it after His six days' work of Creation, the work of Creation was distributed among six days,
followed by a day of rest; *because* the week, ended by the
Sabbath, already existed as an institution, and the writer
wished to adjust artificially the work of Creation to it. In
other words, the week determined the "days" of Creation,
not the "days" of Creation the week.[1]

The story of Paradise and the Fall, on the validity of
which a fundamental part of Christian dogma rests,
"exhibits also points of contact with Babylonia, though
not so definite or complete as those presented by the
first Creation-story." "Eden itself," remarks Professor
Sayce, "is the Babylonian Eden or Chaldean 'plain';
its garden with the Tree of Knowledge is celebrated in
an old Babylonian poem (and depicted on Assyrian
monuments), and two of the rivers that water it are the
Tigris and Euphrates."[2] The cherubim are "clearly no
native Hebrew conception," and are probably derived

---

[1] *Authority and Archæology*, p. 18.
[2] *The Temple Bible*, Introd. p. xiv.

either from the Hittite griffin or the Babylonian divine winged bulls.[1]

In the story of the Flood "we have a direct and interesting parallel from Babylonia," the original of which was discovered in 1872. Canon Driver supplies an admirable *résumé* of the epic, whose subject is the exploits of the hero Gilgamesh, told in twelve cantos. The Deluge-story forms the eleventh of these cantos.

There are of course differences ; the Biblical account of the Deluge was not, any more than the Biblical account of Creation, transcribed directly from a Babylonian source ; but by some channel or other—we can but speculate by what — the Babylonian story found its way into Israel ; details were forgotten or modified : it assumed, of course, a Hebrew complexion, being adapted to the spirit of Hebrew monotheism, and made a vehicle for the higher teaching of the Hebrew religion ; but the main outline remained the same, and the substantial identity of the two narratives is unquestionable.[2]

As for the historical existence of the "Father of the Faithful" and other ancestors of Israel, Canon Driver animadverts as follows on the assumptions of pseudo-concessionists of the type of Professor Sayce :—

Mr Tomkins and Professor Sayce have produced works on *The Age of Abraham* and *Patriarchal Palestine*, full of interesting particulars, collected from the monuments, respecting the condition, political, social, and religious, of

---

[1] *Encyclopædia Biblica*, Art. "Cherubim."
[2] *Authority and Archæology*, p. 27 ; and see *Coll. Essays*, iv. pp. 239-286.

Babylonia, Palestine, and Egypt, in the centuries before the
age of Moses; but neither of these volumes contains the
smallest evidence that either Abraham or the other patriarchs ever actually existed. *Patriarchal Palestine*, in fact,
opens with a fallacy. Critics, it is said, have taught "that
there were no Patriarchs and no Patriarchal age, but, the
critics notwithstanding, the Patriarchal age has actually
existed," and "it has been shown by modern discovery to
be a fact." Modern discovery has shown no such thing.
It has shown, indeed, that Palestine had inhabitants before
the Mosaic age, that Babylonians, Egyptians, and Canaan-
ites, for instance, visited it, or made it their home ; but that
the Hebrew patriarchs lived in it there is no tittle of monu-
mental evidence whatever. They may have done so ; but
our knowledge of the fact depends at present entirely upon
what is said in the Book of Genesis. Not one of the many
facts adduced by Professor Sayce is independent evidence
that the Patriarchs visited Palestine—or even that they
existed at all.[1]

Canon Driver will find materials for stronger criticism
of Professor Sayce in the Introduction contributed by
the latter to the *Temple Bible*, wherein not only Abraham,
but Adam and Noah, are said "to form successive links
in the chain of Divine education, which with each fresh
starting-point becomes less general and more personal."[2]
In the third of his Yale Lectures on *Modern Criticism
and the Preaching of the Old Testament*, Professor G.
A. Smith is in agreement with Canon Driver :—

While archæology has richly illustrated the main outlines
of the Book of Genesis from Abraham to Joseph, it has
not one whit of proof to offer for the personal existence or
characters of the Patriarchs themselves. This is the whole

---

[1] *Authority and Archæology*, p. 149.   [2] P. 15.

change archæology has wrought : it has given us a back-ground and an atmosphere for the stories of Genesis ; it is unable to recall or to certify their heroes.

The legendary character of the patriarchal age, which may be compared with the heroic age in Greece, was demonstrated by Kuenen, Knappert, and other Con-tinental scholars thirty years ago. " Actual ancestors are never distinctly traceable," says Dillmann, a sound statement pushed to extremes by Goldziher, who, follow-ing the late Professor Max Müller's philological methods, resolved Abraham, Isaac, and Jacob into sun and sky myths, Jacob's twelve sons being the moon and eleven stars. Steinthal, with more warrant, converted Samson, the "shining one," into a solar hero whose labours correspond to those of Hercules. But such specula-tions are of slight importance, since the major fact of the unhistorical foundation of the early Hebrew narra-tives is admitted. Canon Driver represents the views accepted by every modern scholar having claim to authority. They are adopted by the contributors to the *Encyclopædia Biblica*[1]—a work in which Huxley would have found the justification of all for which he contended ; they are in course of adoption in text-books, and will, at no long interval, be quietly admitted into " Bible helps " and suchlike manuals issued by the orthodox publishing societies. In the preface to the most recent *History of the Hebrews*, its author, the Rev.

[1] Edited by Canon Cheyne, Oriel Professor of the Interpretation of Holy Scripture in the University of Oxford, and J. Sutherland Black, LL.D.

R. L. Ottley, says : " It is well to recognise the fact that the patriarchal period is described to us in narratives which were compiled in their present form about a thousand years later than the events they describe, and of which, therefore, as Professor G. A. Smith truly observes, 'it is simply impossible for us at this time of day to establish the accuracy.' "

When the source of the cosmogonic and other legends was discovered, it was assumed that their presence in the Old Testament was due to the contact of the Jews with Babylonian ideas during the Exile. But this did not account for the very great modifications which the legends had undergone before their adoption into the final redaction of the Pentateuch—modifications involving long processes of elimination of polytheistic elements. Happily, the discovery of a number of cuneiform tablets at Tel-el-Amarna in Egypt in 1887 throws light upon the difficulty. They show that, at about 1400 B.C.,

Palestine and the neighbouring countries formed an Egyptian province under the rule of Egyptian governors, stationed in the principal towns, and (what is more remarkable) communicating with their superiors in the *Babylonian* language, thus affording conclusive evidence that for long previously Canaan had been under Babylonian influence.[1]

It is therefore in the highest degree probable that the Babylonian legends had been imported into Canaan before the fifteenth century B.C., and that on the settlement of the Israelites in that country, they incorporated

[1] *Authority and Archæology*, p. 72.

these legends into their stock of traditions.   Down to
the eighth century B.C., the materials of Israelitic history
existed only in fragmentary and unsettled form, made up
of songs celebrating the deeds and prowess of heroes;
of scraps of law; and of legendary and actual history
gathered from different sources and spread over many
centuries.   To these inchoate materials priestly and
prophetic hands gave shape, the one laying stress
on the ceremonial law, the other laying stress on
the moral law, but both emphasising the supremacy
of Jahveh, who, after slow emergence from the nature-
stage as a mountain-god, manifest in fire and burn-
ing-bush, had become invested with an awful holi-
ness.   Every song and saga was adapted to "the law,
the prophets, and the writings," and charged with the
conviction of the mission of Israel as the chosen nation;
and hence its religion must be studied in the light of
its history, and its history in the light of its religion.
Despite these admissions, of which sufficing examples
have been given, we find Canon Driver and his brother
theologians still justifying Huxley's gravamen in devoting
themselves

to the end of keeping the name of " Inspiration " to suggest
the divine source, and consequent infallibility, of more or
less of the Biblical literature, while carefully emptying the
term of any definite sense. For "plenary inspiration" we
are asked to substitute a sort of "inspiration with limited
liability," the limit being susceptible of indefinite fluctuation
in correspondence with the demands of scientific criticism.
When this advances that at once retreats.

This Parthian policy is carried out with some dexterity;
but, like other such manœuvres in the face of a strong foe,
it seems likely to end in disaster. It is easy to say, and
sounds plausible, that the Bible was not meant to teach
anything but ethics and religion, and that its utterances on
other matters are mere *obiter dicta:* it is also a specious
suggestion that inspiration, filtering through human brains,
must undergo a kind of fallibility contamination; and that
this human impurity is responsible for any errors, the existence of which has to be admitted, however unwillingly.

But how does the apologist know what the Biblical
writers intended to teach, and what they did not intend
to teach? And even if their authority is restricted to
matters of faith and morals, who is prepared to deny that
the story of the fabrication of Eve, that of the lapse of
innocence effected by a talking snake, that of the Deluge
and demonological legends, have exercised, and still exercise,
a profound influence on Christian theology and Christian
ethics?[1]

Here Huxley again reaches the core of the matter.
There was a consistency in the old theory of verbal
inspiration; there is none in the theory of a divine and
human element in the Scriptures, since there is no
possible test by which the one can be distinguished
from the other. And the decision as to what is, and as
to what is not, revelation, would hardly have been left
by the Holy Spirit to the creed-makers and the critics.
When Canon Driver speaks of the "spirit of the legend
of the Creation being changed in the light of revelation," and of the Israelite writer as "gifted by the Holy
Spirit"; when Professor Sayce says that "the language

[1] *Coll. Essays*, iv. p. viii.

of Genesis rises to the height of the revelation it contains," and when Mr Ottley talks of the " inspiration which we justly attribute to the Old Testament writers," they are each playing with names to which there are no correspondent realities. As Professor Goldwin Smith puts it—

If it was from the Holy Spirit that these narratives emanated, how can the Holy Spirit have failed to let mankind know that in reality they were allegories? How could it allow them to be received as literal truths, to mislead the world for ages, to bar the advance of science, and, when science at last prevailed, to discredit revelation by the exposure? Besides, to maintain the symbolical truths of Genesis is almost as hard as to maintain its literal truth.[1]

Obviously, the effort to retain the saving clause of a revelation in a miscellaneous collection of writings of uncertain date and authorship, and of disputed meaning, is due to the fact that the Christian doctrine of the Atonement is bound up with the story of the Fall. The legend of Eden is the keystone of the arch which supports the whole Christian scheme of redemption, and the evidence of palæontology has disproved the Pauline teaching that " death came into the world by sin."

But, in the meantime, while the learned among them still hesitate to follow facts to their only possible conclusion, the great mass of the unlearned clergy will have warrant for the indiscriminate reading of the legends of a talking ass; an arrested sun; of the stories of Simeon

[1] *Guesses at the Riddle of Existence*, p. 55.

and Levi's treachery and Jehu's butcheries; of the high
ethical teaching of the Prophets; and of the beatitudes
on the meek, the peacemakers, and the pure in heart—
as equally integral parts of writings inspired "by the
Holy Spirit." Every Sunday in thousands of churches
their congregations are still told that "God Himself
spake all these words, saying, In six days the Lord
made heaven and earth, the sea, and all that in them is,
and rested the seventh day : wherefore the Lord blessed
the Sabbath day, and hallowed it." [1] Thus, as Emerson
says, "a vast carcass of tradition is exhibited every year
with as much solemnity as a new revelation."

Criticism was not to be arrested by the blank page
which separates Malachi from Matthew; but opprobrium
greeted the critic.[2]

Destroy the foundation of most forms of dogmatic Christianity contained in the second chapter of Genesis, if you
will; the new ecclesiasticism undertakes to underpin the
structure, and make it, at any rate to the eye, as firm as
ever; but let him be anathema who applies exactly the
same canons of criticism to the opening chapters of
"Matthew" or of "Luke." School children may be told that

---

[1] The clergy "are either propagating what they may easily know,
and therefore are bound to know, to be falsities; or, if they use
the words in some non-natural sense, they fall below the moral
standard of the much-abused Jesuit."—*Coll. Essays*, ii. p. 146.

[2] Bishop (then Canon) Gore admits that the same criticism must
be applied to the New Testament as is applied to the Old, but he
qualifies this with the cryptic remark that "because the historical
and literary conditions in the two cases are in general very different,
the result also will be in general very different."—*Pilot*, 10th Aug.
1901.

the world was by no means made in six days, and that
implicit belief in the story of Noah's Ark is permissible
only, as a matter of business, to their toymakers ; but they
are to hold for the certaintest of truths, to be doubted only
at peril of their salvation, that their Galilean fellow-child
Jesus, nineteen centuries ago, had no human father.[1]

In treating the Old Testament "like any other book,"
Huxley chose as a test case the interview of Saul with
the ghost of Samuel through the medium of a witch.
In treating the New Testament "like any other book,"
he chose as a test case the story of Jesus exorcising
demons from a man and permitting them to enter into
two thousand swine, " to the great loss and damage of
the innocent Gadarene owners." In both cases, therefore, the question of the existence of spirits is raised.
His reason for the selection was that in the course of
discussions in the years 1889-1891 "it had been maintained by the defenders of ecclesiastical Christianity that
the demonology of the books of the New Testament is
an essential and integral part of the revelation of the
nature of the spiritual world promulgated by Jesus of
Nazareth." So far he was in agreement with them.

Belief in spirits, good and bad, guardian angels and
maliceful demons, beings filling an intermediate place as
lower than gods and greater than men, is a survival of
savage ideas as to the presence of innumerable spirits
everywhere, and an impulse in certain directions was
given to this belief among the Jews during the Exile.

[1] *Coll. Essays*, v. p. xi.

M

The ancient Babylonian idea that disease is due to demons (a belief common to barbaric peoples, among whom disease and death are not regarded as natural events), whose expulsion was the business of the exorcist, struck root in Judaism, and hence we find that the references to evil spirits are more frequent in the New Testament than in the Old. "Belief in possession is distinctive of late Jewish times,"[1] as is that in angels, who become the appointed "messengers" between Jahveh and men; on whose duties as servants before the heavenly throne the prophets, notably Ezekiel and Zechariah, enlarge; and whose presence as attendants on the "Son of man" at the Judgement-Day is dwelt upon by Jesus.

It is plain as language can make it, that the writers of the Gospels believed in the existence of Satan and the subordinate ministers of evil as strongly as they believed in that of God and the angels; and that they had an unhesitating faith in possession and in exorcism. No reader of the first three Gospels can hesitate to admit that, in the opinion of those persons among whom the traditions out of which they are compiled arose, Jesus held, and constantly acted upon, the same theory of the spiritual world. Nowhere do we find the slightest hint that he doubted the theory, or questioned the efficacy of the curative operations based upon it.[2]

The writer of the article "Demons" in the *Encyclopædia Biblica* says: "There is no sign on the part of Jesus, any more than on the part of the evangelists, of mere accommodation to the current belief. It is true that 'Satan'

[1] *Encyclopædia Biblica*: Art. "Demons."
[2] *Coll. Essays*, v. p. 193.

is used metaphorically in the rebuke of Peter (Matt. xvi. 23) and that 'unclean spirit' is figurative in Matt. xii. 43. Acceptance of the current belief is clearly at the basis of the argument of Jesus with the Pharisees (Luke xi. 16-26); . . . and that he believed in the power of others besides himself and his disciples to expel demons, in some sense at any rate, seems clear in the presence of such passages as Matt. xii. 27 and Luke xi. 19, where he attributes the power to the disciples of the Pharisees. He recognises also the fact that similar success was attained by some who used his name without actually following him (Mark ix. 38) or without being more than professed disciples." [1] And the author of *Exploratio Evangelica* says that "it is probable Jesus accepted the hypothesis of demoniac possession as easily as he accepted the hypothesis that the sun moves round the earth." [2] In the declaration that he cast out devils (Luke xiii. 32), and his bestowal of the like power upon his disciples (Luke ix. 1) ; in the story of the temptation ; in the warning that the wicked would depart into everlasting fire, prepared for the devil and his angels ("the doctrine of eternal damnation is a Judaistic survival of grossly immoral character" [3]), no ingenuity can distort the fact that Jesus shared the common demonological belief of his time and people.

[1] See quotation to the same effect, from Dr Alexander's *Bibl. Cyclopædia*, given in *Coll. Essays*, v. p. 217.
[2] P. 225.
[3] *A Critical History of a Future Life.* By R. H. Charles, D.D., p. 311.

And the issue which Huxley raised is as clear as it is serious :—

When such a story as that about the Gadarene swine is placed before us, the importance of the decision, whether it is to be accepted or rejected, cannot be overestimated. If the demonological part of it is to be accepted, the authority of Jesus is unmistakably pledged to the demonological system current in Judea in the first century. The belief in devils, who possess men and can be transferred from men to pigs, becomes as much a part of Christian dogma as any article of the creeds. If it is to be rejected, there are two alternative conclusions. Supposing the Gospels to be historically accurate, it follows that Jesus shared in the errors respecting the nature of the spiritual world prevalent in the age in which he lived, and among the people of his nation. If, on the other hand, the Gospel traditions give us only a popular version of the sayings and doings of Jesus, falsely coloured, and distorted by the superstitious imaginings of the minds through which it had passed, what guarantee have we that a similar unconscious falsification, in accordance with preconceived ideas, may not have taken place in respect of other reported sayings and doings? What is to prevent a conscientious inquirer from finding himself at last in a purely agnostic position with respect to the teachings of Jesus, and consequently with respect to the fundamentals of Christianity?[1]

The old argument that miracles are impossible, because contrary to the order of nature, is no longer advanced, since its force is limited to what we infer from our experience of that order. The fact that a certain thing has not happened within our knowledge is no proof that it never happened in the past, or that it can never happen in the future. Nothing, as Huxley points out, is to be

---

[1] *Coll. Essays*, v. pp. 193, 194 ; and see p. 218.

declared "impossible," except contradictions in terms, as a round square, a present past, or the intersection of two parallel lines. None of us have seen a centaur or a griffin, but the existence of such monsters is conceivable; so with the miracles reported in the Old and New Testaments or in the *Acta Sanctorum*—they are conceivable by the imagination, however repellent to the reason. And the argument which alone has force against miracles is, that as their alleged occurrence is an event lying outside our experience of an unbroken uniformity of nature, belief in them must be determined by the validity of the evidence. And the more improbable the character of the alleged miracle, the more cogent must be the evidence in its support. Dealing with the miracles narrated in the Gospels, it would seem only reasonable, before accepting the truth of the story, to expect that in the case of documents for which inspiration is claimed there should be no discrepancies in the record; that the Holy Spirit would have protected the revelation from error and obscurity. Under this test the evidence breaks down. An examination of a work published by the Religious Tract Society, under the unconsciously ironical title, *Harmony of the Gospels*, brings out the discord between them. Upon a matter so momentous in its assumed bearings on human destiny as the Virgin Birth (to which the earliest of the Synoptics makes no reference) there is no agreement; while the accounts of the character of the last supper, of the last hours of Jesus on the cross, and of the events following his

alleged resurrection, vary irreconcilably. A recent
defender of the faith remarks that " the tale of the
physical resurrection of Jesus belongs evidently to the
same circle of thought as that of the miraculous birth.
It shows a love of the marvellous ; is deeply tinged with
materialism ; and rests on a historical substruction which
falls to pieces on a careful examination." [1] So with the
Gadarene story ; so with the story of the feeding of
several thousand with a few loaves, with the result that
" the quantity of the fragments of the meal left over
amounted to much more than the original store " : the
reports differ.   The explanation, hitherto arrested and
darkened by theories of inspiration, is obvious.   With
the abandonment of those theories every difficulty
vanishes.   The Gospels are the handiwork of men who
lived in an age when any conception of the uniformity
of nature was foreign to the mind ; men in whom the
critical faculty of weighing of evidence was wholly lacking,
and who set down, each in his own fashion, stories of
events said to have happened many years before—stories
which had therefore filtered through many channels ;
fallible hearers repeating them to fallible writers, whose
honesty and sincerity are not doubted, but whose com-
petency is questioned.

As Dr Sutherland Black says in his admirably com-
pendious article on the " Gospels " in *Chambers's Encyclopædia*, " no one of them is a primary document in the
sense of having been written in its present form from

[1] *Exploratio Evangelica*, p. 255.

direct personal knowledge; and it is obvious that each succeeding evangelist, in availing himself of the labours of his predecessors, did so with a feeling of perfect freedom, not claiming for himself, nor according to his fellows, nor expecting for either from the church, any title to authority as infallible." That authority was claimed for them by the framers of the Canon, fallible men determining what is infallible; men whose critical capacity and materials for decision are hardly warrant for the burden which they have for centuries, unchallenged, laid upon more competent judges. "The times of the first Church were times of excitement; when the appeal was not to the questioning, thinking understanding, but to unheeding, all-venturing emotion, to that lower class 'from whom faiths ascend'; not to the cultivated class by whom they are criticised." [1]   Huxley's tribute to the service rendered to human kind by the Bible (see *ante*, p. 34) adds emphasis to his protest against the evil of which the doctrine of its infallibility has been fruitful.

The pretension to infallibility, by whomsoever made, has done endless mischief; with impartial malignity it has proved a curse alike to those who have made it and those who have accepted it : and its most baneful shape is book infallibility. For sacerdotal corporations and schools of philosophy are able, under due compulsion of opinion, to retreat from positions that have became untenable; while the dead hand of a book sets and stiffens, amidst texts and formulæ, until it becomes a mere petrifaction, fit only for the

---

[1] *Literary Studies.* By Walter Bagehot, ii. p. 46.

function of stumbling-block which it so admirably performs. Wherever bibliolatry has prevailed, bigotry and cruelty have accompanied it. It lies at the root of the deep-seated, sometimes disguised, but never absent, antagonism of all the varieties of ecclesiasticism to the freedom of thought and to the spirit of scientific investigation. For those who look upon ignorance as one of the chief sources of evil, and hold veracity, not merely in act but in thought, to be the one condition of true progress, whether moral or intellectual, it is clear that the Biblical idol must go the way of all other idols. Of infallibility in all shapes, lay or clerical, it is needful to iterate with more than Catonic pertinacity, *Delenda est.*[1]

In the controversy over the Gadarene story, the authenticity of which was defended by Dr Wace and Mr Gladstone, Huxley raised the question whether the ever-accumulating experience of mankind concerning the non-intrusion of the supernatural in the sequence of phenomena was to be regarded as of no account as against the story of demon-possessed pigs. For history shows that all advance in knowledge has caused recession of belief in miracle, and that the farther back inquiry is pushed the more active is that belief. And the argument that miracles ceased at a certain stage, the date of which is a hotly debated question among ecclesiastics, has no force if they were wrought as signs and wonders to remove unbelief, since if that was their purpose the need of them is greater than ever. As was his wont, Huxley went straight to the point.

I am not more certain about anything than I am that the

---

[1] *Coll. Essays*, iv. p. 10.

evidence tendered in favour of the demonology of which the Gaderene story is a typical example is utterly valueless.[1]

Everything that I know of physiological and pathological science leads me to entertain a very strong conviction that the phenomena ascribed to possession are as purely natural as those which constitute small-pox ; everything that I know of anthropology leads me to think that the belief in demons and demoniacal possession is a mere survival of a once universal superstition, and that its persistence at the present time is pretty much in the inverse ratio of the general instruction, intelligence, and sound judgement of the population among whom it prevails. Everything that I know of law and justice convinces me that the wanton destruction of other people's property is a misdemeanour of evil example. Again, the study of history, and especially of the fifteenth, sixteenth, and seventeenth centuries, leaves no shadow of doubt on my mind that the belief in the reality of possession and of witchcraft, justly based, alike by Catholics and Protestants, upon this and innumerable other passages in both the Old and New Testaments, gave rise, through the special influence of Christian ecclesiastics, to the most horrible persecutions and judicial murders of thousands upon thousands of innocent men, women, and children. And when I reflect that the record of a plain and simple declaration upon such an occasion as this, that the belief in witchcraft and possession is wicked nonsense, would have rendered the long agony of medieval humanity impossible, I am prompted to reject, as dishonouring, the supposition that such declaration was withheld out of condescension to popular error.[2]

. . . .

The Gospels, the Acts, the Epistles, and the Apocalypse assert the existence of the devil, of his demons and of hell, as plainly as they do that of God and his angels and heaven. It is plain that the Messianic and the Satanic conceptions of the writers of these books are the obverse and the reverse of

---

[1] *Coll. Essays,* v. p. 206.   [2] *Ib.,* pp. 215, 216.

the same intellectual coinage. If we turn from Scripture to
the traditions of the Fathers and the confessions of the
Churches, it will appear that, in this one particular, at any
rate, time has brought about no important deviation from
primitive belief. From Justin onwards it may often be a
fair question whether God, or the devil, occupies a larger
share of the attention of the Fathers. It is the devil who
instigates the Roman authorities to persecute ; the gods and
goddesses of paganism are devils, and idolatry itself is an
invention of Satan ; if a saint falls away from grace, it is by
the seduction of the demon ; if heresy arises, the devil has
suggested it ; and some of the Fathers go so far as to challenge the pagans to a sort of exorcising match, by way of
testing the truth of Christianity. Medieval Christianity is
at one with patristic, on this head. The masses, the clergy,
the theologians, and the philosophers alike, live and move
and have their being in a world full of demons, in which
sorcery and possession are everyday occurrences. Nor did
the Reformation make any difference. Whatever else Luther
assailed, he left the traditional demonology untouched ; nor
could any one have entertained a more hearty and un-
compromising belief in the devil than he and, at a later
period, the Calvinistic fanatics of New England did.
Finally, in these last years of the nineteenth century, the
demonological hypotheses of the first century are, explicitly
or implicitly, held and occasionally acted upon by the
immense majority of Christians of all confessions.[1]

But although this be so with the loose adherents of
current creeds ; although the man who smiles when he
hears the story of the demons passing into the bodies of
terrified swine has a trembling of soul when he hears of
the temptation of Jesus by the devil, so that, feeling
scepticism to be somewhat perilous, he carries his belief

[1] *Coll. Essays*, v. pp. 322, 323.

in demonology to a "suspense account," Huxley added that he ventured "to doubt whether, at this present moment, any Protestant theologian who has a reputation to lose will say that he believes the Gadarene story."

Dr Wace at once retorted that, so far as he was concerned, the doubt had no foundation. "I repeat," he said, "that I believe it, and that Mr Huxley has removed the only objection to my believing it," namely, that to reject it would be denial of the veracity of Jesus. While humorously disclaiming any responsibility for the confirmation of Dr Wace's belief that "the spiritual world comprises devils, who, under certain circumstances, may enter men and be transferred from them to four-footed beasts,"[1] Huxley could but admire the courage, whatever might be the opinion he held of the intelligence, of his opponent. "Dr Wace," he said, "has raised for himself a monument *ære perennius.*" Huxley was charitably silent as to the appropriate inscription to be put on it.

In the attack upon agnosticism which led to the controversy, Dr Wace accused the agnostics of thus dubbing themselves to avoid the "unpleasant significance" attaching to the term "infidel," which, like "freethinker," strange as it may seem in this twentieth century, still appears to convey reproach. And he added, in minatory tartness, that "it is, and ought to be, an unpleasant thing for a man to have to say

[1] *Coll. Essays,* v. p. 415.

plainly that he does not believe in Jesus Christ."[1]
Whatever vague threat the word "unpleasant" might
convey, whether hints of the secular arm, or social
ostracism, or eternal punishment, any possible penalty
was not likely to weigh with Huxley. He retorted
that the proposition

that "it ought to be" unpleasant for any man to say anything
which he sincerely and, after due deliberation, believes, is,
to my mind, of the most profoundly immoral character. I
verily believe that the great good which has been effected in
the world by Christianity has been largely counteracted by
the pestilent doctrine on which all the Churches have in-
sisted, that honest disbelief in their more or less astonishing
creeds is a moral offence, indeed a sin of the deepest dye,
deserving and involving the same future retribution as
murder and robbery. If we could only see, in one view, the
torrents of hypocrisy and cruelty, the lies, the slaughter, the
violations of every obligation of humanity, which have flowed
from this source along the course of the history of Christian
nations, our worst imaginations of hell would pale beside the
vision.[2]

As to the use of the term "agnostic," Huxley says—

When I reached intellectual maturity and began to ask
myself whether I was an atheist, a theist, or a pantheist;
a materialist or an idealist; a Christian or a freethinker; I
found that the more I learned and reflected, the less ready
was the answer; until, at last, I came to the conclusion that
I had neither art nor part with any of these denominations,
except the last. The one thing in which most of these
good people were agreed was the one thing in which I
differed from them. They were quite sure they had attained

---

[1] *Coll. Essays*, v. p. 210.   [2] *Ib.*, p. 241.

a certain " gnosis,"—had, more or less successfully, solved the problem of existence ; while I was quite sure I had not, and had a pretty strong conviction that the problem was insoluble.[1]

At any rate, whatever explanation of the universe there may be, Huxley was satisfied that theology had not supplied it. Joining the Metaphysical Society, he found in that "remarkable confraternity of antagonists" every variety of philosophical and theological opinion represented, most of the members being " -ists of one sort or another." So, nameless himself, he " conceived the appropriate title of " agnostic."   " It came," he says, " into my head as suggestively antithetic to the ' gnostic ' of Church history, who professed to know so much about the very things of which I was ignorant."   But, as the word implies, it connotes neither confession of faith nor doctrinal formula ; neither affirmation nor denial.   " And dares stamp nothing false where he finds nothing sure." [2]

Agnosticism, in fact, is not a creed, but a method, the essence of which lies in the rigorous application of a single principle. That principle is of great antiquity ; it is as old as Socrates ; as old as the writer who said, " Try all things, hold fast by that which is good " ; it is the foundation of the Reformation, which simply illustrated the axiom that every man should be able to give a reason for the faith that is in him ; it is the great principle of Descartes ; it is the fundamental axiom of modern science. Positively, the principle may be expressed : In matters of the intellect, follow your reason as far as it will take you, without regard to any other

---

[1] *Coll. Essays*, v. p. 238.   [2] Matthew Arnold, *Empedocles.*

consideration. And negatively : In matters of the intellect do not pretend that conclusions are certain which are not demonstrated or demonstrable. That I take to be the agnostic faith, which if a man keep whole and undefiled, he shall not be ashamed to look the universe in the face, whatever the future may have in store for him.[1]

It was no hard matter to show that the vagueness was on the other side. The phrase "belief in Jesus Christ" has as many meanings as there are sects. The Episcopalian has one definition of it ; the Unitarian has another. And Huxley showed what difficulty attends any effort to construct a consistent portrait of Jesus from the Synoptics and the gospel of John, and then to reconcile this with the Jesus of the creeds. The New Testament witnesses to disruptions on the question of "belief" in him soon after his death. His immediate followers were "Nazarenes," who acknowledged his brother James as their head, and who conformed to the Jewish law, differing from their copatriots only in believing that the Messiah had already come in the person of Jesus. The division of the disciples of the Master into Nazarenes and Christians, which latter appellation is said to have been first used at Antioch, arose through the contention of Paul and Barnabas that the commands regarding circumcision and abstinence from certain foods were abrogated. So the "primitive Church," around whose story ecclesiastical historians have cast a halo, was "no dogmatic dovecot pervaded by the most loving unity and doctrinal harmony." Nazarenism

[1] *Coll. Essays*, v. p. 245 ; and see *ante*, p. 40.

became "a damnable heresy, while the younger doctrine throve and pushed out its shoots into that endless variety of sects, of which the three strongest survivors are the Roman and Greek Churches and modern Protestantism."[1]

A masterly summary of the rise and development of Christianity, of the foreign influences which shaped it, and of the mythologies, the pagan rites and ceremonies, themselves of barbaric origin, which it incorporated, is given in the essay on the "Evolution of Theology."[2] This should be read in conjunction with the prologue to the fifth volume of *Collected Essays* (of which Huxley wrote to a friend, "It cost me more time and pains than any equal number of pages I have ever written "[3]), in which the history of the struggle between Naturalism and Supernaturalism is outlined, and the evidence on which the doctrine of Evolution rests, set forth. Both papers will help to clear away the haze which hangs round questions in the discussion of which the spirit of the advocate rather than of the truth-seeker is present. Strauss said that "the true criticism of dogma is its history," because in this are to be found the indictment of humanity against creeds between which and the facts of life and nature there is no correspondence, since they remain puzzles to the head and strangers to the heart. As Emerson says, "The prayers and dogmas of our Church are like the zodiac of Denderah and the astronomical monuments of the

---

[1] *Coll. Essays*, v. p. 231.   [2] *Ib.*, pp. 367-371.   [3] II. 298.

Hindoos, wholly insulated from anything now extant in
the life and the business of the people." [1]

In place of the "tangled Trinities," the logomachies
which only bewilder and perplex, Huxley asked the
Churches to revive "a conception of religion which," he
says, "appears to me as wonderful an inspiration of
genius as the art of Pheidias or the science of Aristotle.
'And what doth the Lord require of thee, but to do
justly, and to love mercy, and to walk humbly with thy
God?' If any so-called religion takes away from this
great saying of Micah, I think it wantonly mutilates,
while, if it adds thereto, I think it obscures the perfect
ideal of religion." [2]

All that is best in the ethics of the modern world, in so
far as it has not grown out of Greek thought or Barbarian
manhood, is the direct development of the ethics of old
Israel. There is no code of legislation, ancient or modern,
at once so just and so merciful, so tender to the weak and
poor, as the Jewish law; and if the Gospels are to be
trusted, Jesus of Nazareth himself declared that he taught
nothing but that which lay implicitly, or explicitly, in the
religious and ethical system of his people.
And the scribe said unto him, Of a truth, Teacher, thou
hast well said that he is one; and there is none other but
he; and to love him with all the heart, and with all the
understanding, and with all the strength, and to love his
neighbour as himself, is much more than all whole burnt
offerings and sacrifices (Mark xii. 32, 33).
Here is the briefest of summaries of the teaching of
the prophets of Israel of the eighth century; does the
Teacher, whose doctrine is thus set forth in his presence,

---

[1] "The American Scholar."   [2] *Coll. Essays*, iv. p. 161.

repudiate the exposition ?   Nay; we are told, on the contrary, that Jesus saw that he "answered discreetly," and replied, "Thou art not far from the kingdom of God."

So that I think that even if the creeds, from the so-called
"Apostles'" to the so-called "Athanasian," were swept into
oblivion ; and even if the human race should arrive at the
conclusion that, whether a bishop washes a cup or leaves it
unwashed, is not a matter of the least consequence, it will
get on very well.   The causes which have led to the development of morality in mankind, which have guided or
impelled us all the way from the savage to the civilised
state, will not cease to operate because a number of ecclesiastical hypotheses turn out to be baseless.   And, even if
the absurd notion that morality is more the child of speculation than of practical necessity and inherited instinct had
any foundation ; if all the world is going to thieve, murder,
and otherwise misconduct itself as soon as it discovers that
certain portions of ancient history are mythical; what is the
relevance of such arguments to any one who holds by the
Agnostic principle ? [1]

Turning briefly to Mr Gladstone's intervention in
the controversy, his chief concern was about Huxley's
charge against Jesus as wantonly destroying other
people's property.   He was sceptical as to the pigs
numbering two thousand, and in a footnote to the
concluding chapter of the *Impregnable Rock of Holy
Scripture* suggests that "so large a number may be due
to the error of a copyist, or very possibly a marginal
gloss, which afterwards crept into the text."   But as the
existence of demons was accepted by Mr Gladstone as a
matter of course, the statistics as to the pigs are of
minor importance, except as they may affect the ques-

[1] *Coll. Essays*, v. p. 316.

N

tion of an inspired text. What he sought to prove was that the keepers of the swine were Jews, and that therefore they were justly punished for their breach of the Mosaic law. Josephus is quoted as evidence. But Huxley showed conclusively that Mr Gladstone had misread Josephus, and he established beyond question that Gadara was a Gentile, and not a Jewish city. All in vain. Mr Gladstone stuck to his statements, and as edition after edition of the *Impregnable Rock* was issued without modification, there can be little wonder that while in publicly criticising these methods Huxley called them "peculiar," in private correspondence he spoke of the man who practised them as a "copious shuffler,"[1] and bracketed him with Owen and Bishop Wilberforce as belonging "to a very curious type of humanity, with many excellent and even great qualities, and one fatal defect—utter untrustworthiness."[2] It is interesting to note here that in a conversation with Mr Lionel Tollemache, Mr Gladstone "denied genius to Huxley, but allowed it to Owen and Romanes"![3]

Among the outside criticisms which the controversy provoked was that which suggested that both disputants "might be better occupied than in fighting over the

---

[1] II. 122. In a letter to Colonel Ingersoll, written in March 1889, Huxley says : "Gladstone's attack on you is one of the best things he has written. I do not think there is more than fifty per cent more verbiage than is necessary, nor any sentence with *more* than two meanings."—*Literary Guide*, December 1901.

[2] II. 341. [3] *Talks with Mr Gladstone.*

Gadarene pigs." Upon this Huxley pertinently commented—

If these too famous swine were the only parties to the suit, I, for my part, should fully admit the justice of the rebuke. But, under the beneficent rule of the Court of Chancery, in former times, it was not uncommon that a quarrel about a few perches of worthless land ended in the ruin of ancient families and the engulfing of great estates; and I think that our admonisher failed to observe the analogy —to note the momentous consequences of the judgement which may be awarded in the present apparently insignificant action *in re* the swineherds of Gadara.

The immediate effect of such judgement will be the decision of the question, whether the men of the nineteenth century are to adopt the demonology of the men of the first century, as divinely revealed truth, or to reject it, as degrading falsity.[1]

Yet, complete as is the discomfiture of the current theology in its conflict with historical criticism of its documents, the *Impregnable Rock of Holy Scripture* remains in demand, and Dr Wace is, we suppose, still a power in the pulpit. The chains of custom and tradition still bind, and indifference still paralyses, the souls of men. In this, and not in active and deep conviction of the truth of its creeds, the strength of orthodoxy lies. It has made unto itself a more sure habitation in yielding to "the form and pressure" of the time; its official representatives have never abandoned that defence of privilege which is of greater moment than defence of what is left of the faith, and the roots of ecclesiastical

[1] *Coll. Essays*, v. p. 414.

institutions have become more closely intertwined with those of the body politic, so that attack upon the one is menace to the other.

Nevertheless, "wisdom is justified of her children." "Much water has flowed under the bridges" since 1864, when a number of clergymen, consistently enough, formulated a declaration of faith that Jesus taught the doctrine of everlasting punishment, and begged their brethren to sign it "for the love of God";[1] or even since 1891, when another group, who had not bowed the knee to the Baal of modern scholarship, affirmed their belief that "the canonical scriptures of the Old and New Testaments declare incontrovertibly the actual historical truth in all records, both of past events and of the delivery of predictions to be thereafter fulfilled."[2] In fact, the abrasion of incredible and inhuman dogmas has gone on at so rapid a rate that belief in them might be thought to be limited to the vulgar and illiterate, were it not for restatements of the following order, which is quoted from the widely circulated worldly and other-worldly *British Weekly*. In commenting on certain articles in the *Encyclopædia Biblica* the reader is advised to "take the Gospels, the Acts, and the Epistles, and erase from them as incredible everything that does not affirm miracle. He will find that the narrative of miracle is so welded with facts and words and in-

[1] *Life and Letters of Dean Stanley*, ii. p. 158.
[2] *Coll. Essays*, v. p. 23.

ferences, that to cut it out is to reduce the whole to a rag-heap." But these strident voices are softened in the atmosphere of the new knowledge. Dogmas are dying —very slowly—as other superstitions have died, because they cannot adapt themselves to changed conditions. They are explained, and their explanation is their doom.

Truly, "wisdom is justified of her children": wellnigh all for which Huxley contended is conceded, and the rest will follow in due time. The admissions as to the unhistorical element in the Bible which are made by modern theologians are not limited to the Old Testament. The great Dictionary of the Bible, already referred to, in which the best scholarship of Britain and the Continent is embodied, and which has as its chief editor "the Oriel Professor of the Interpretation of Holy Scripture at Oxford," contains articles, as quotations have shown already (see p. 178), which a generation ago would have given the Dean of Arches a busy time over trials for heresy. In the article on "Jesus" he is spoken of by the late Dr Bruce as "the child of his time and people"; and, concerning the Passion, the same writer says, "For modern criticism the story, even in its most historic version, is not pure truth, but truth mixed with doubtful legend," although, "when examined with a critical microscope, not a few of the relative incidents stand the test." In the article on the "Gospels" Professor Schmiedel doubts "whether any credible elements are to be found in them," and from the entire body of the reported sayings of Jesus he chooses five passages which, it is suggested, may form "foundation-pillars for a truly scientific life of Jesus," in whom, Professor Schmiedel adds, "we have to do with a completely human being. The divine is to be sought in him only in the form in which it is capable of being found in a man." Of the Fourth Gospel, which he places towards the latter half of the second century, this estimate is given—

A book which begins by declaring Jesus to be the *logos* of God, and ends by representing a cohort of Roman soldiers as falling to the ground at the majesty of his appearance, and by representing one hundred pounds of ointment as having been used at his embalming, ought by these facts alone to be spared such a misunderstanding of its true character as would be implied in supposing that it meant to be a historical work.

After such strong meat it would seem but the offering of milk to babes for the writers to suggest that the narrative of the blasting of the fig-tree by Jesus has "improbabilities which are obvious and cannot be explained away," or that in the Zaccheus incident "there are difficulties in the way of conceding more than an ideal truth to this delightful story."

From these concessions there is but a short step to the larger concessions of the school of Schleiermacher, revived by Sabatier, Gardner, and others, who base Christianity on the facts of religious experience, transferring, as the last-named writer explains, "the support of Christian doctrine from history to psychology, from the history of facts to the history of ideas." Upon which the obvious comment is that the adherents of every other religion may find equal validity for it in the facts of their experience.

V.

THE CONSTRUCTOR.

In the prologue to his Controversial Essays Huxley says, " I have hitherto dwelt upon scientific Naturalism chiefly in its critical and destructive aspect. But the present incarnation of the spirit of the Renascence differs from its predecessor in the eighteenth century in that it builds up as well as pulls down." [1] What the structure should be is indicated in his controversy with Mr Gladstone, and to this may be added a passage from a letter to Mr Romanes :—

I have a great respect for the Nazarenism of Jesus—very little for later "Christianity." But the only religion that makes appeal to me is prophetic Judaism. Add to it something from the best Stoics, and something from Spinoza, and something from Goethe, and there is a religion for men. Some of these days I think I will make a cento out of the works of these people. [2]

The Hebrew prophets made special appeal to him, since, "to do justly, to love mercy, and to walk humbly before thy God" was to base religion on the stable foundation of human relations. There would be no need to

[1] *Coll. Essays*, v. p. 41.   [2] II. 339.

omit the last words of that verse, because the doctrine of evolution is not necessarily anti-theistic

It does not even come into contact with Theism, considered as a philosophical doctrine. That with which it does collide, and with which it is absolutely inconsistent, is the conception of creation which theological speculators have based upon the history narrated in the opening of the book of Genesis. There is a great deal of talk and not a little lamentation about the so-called religious difficulties which physical science has created. In theological science, as a matter of fact, it has created none. Not a solitary problem presents itself to the philosophical Theist at the present day, which has not existed from the time that philosophers began to think out the logical grounds and the logical consequences of Theism. All the real or imaginary perplexities which flow from the conception of the universe as a determinate mechanism, are equally involved in the assumption of an Eternal, Omnipotent, and Omniscient Deity. The theological equivalent of the scientific conception of order is Providence ; and the doctrine of determinism follows as surely from the attributes of foreknowledge assumed by the theologian, as from the universality of natural causation assumed by the man of science. The angels in 'Paradise Lost' would have found the task of enlightening Adam upon the mysteries of " Fate, Foreknowledge, and Free-will" not a whit more difficult, if their pupil had been educated in a "Real-schule," and trained in every laboratory of a modern university. In respect of the great problems of philosophy the post-Darwinian generation is, in one sense, exactly where the præ-Darwinian generation were. They remain insoluble. But the present generation has the advantage of being better provided with the means of freeing itself from the tyranny of certain sham solutions.[1]

---

[1] Huxley's chapter in Darwin's *Life and Letters*, ii. p. 203 ; and cf. ii. p. 302.

What Renan says of Marcus Aurelius applies to Huxley : " He resolutely severed moral beauty from all definite theology; he did not permit duty to depend on any metaphysical opinions concerning a First Cause." Hence his opposition to the theory of morals as innate, and as of supernatural origin. Every man, it is held by the intuitive school, is born with the faculty of discerning right from wrong, while, superfluous as this would seem, the declaration of what actions are right and what actions are wrong is to be found in divinely given codes, of which that of the Ten Words or Commandments is cited as an example. Hence springs the wellnigh universal belief in the interdependence of morals and dogma—the belief that to err in the one is to err in the other. Hence, also, the historical accuracy of the narrative being assumed, the belief that man's power of choice as a free agent between good and evil was first exercised in Eden.[1]   Less momentous, according to current theories of the consequence of Adam's fall to mankind, but more impressive, was the scene at the foot of Mount Sinai, when Jahveh made known through Moses that he would appear in "a thick cloud," so that the people might hear him when he spoke to their leader. And they beheld, the writer of Exodus narrates, the descent of the god in fire upon the mountain, when

[1] The essence of that which is improperly called the freewill doctrine is that occasionally, at any rate, human volition is self-caused, that is to say, not caused at all ; for to cause oneself one must have anteceded oneself—which is, to say the least of it, difficult to imagine.—*Coll. Essays,* ix. p. 142.

"God spake all these words" of the Ten Commandments, and wrote them with his own finger upon two
tables of stone. Thus, in a code, the legend of whose
divine origin is accepted throughout Christendom, the
making of images and murder, the breaking of the
seventh day of the week as a rest-day and theft, are
put upon the same plane of ethics, and the confusion
between sin against man and offences against ritual
emphasised.

Human nature being what it is, the supersession of
theories of ethical codes as integral parts of revelation
seems as far off as the Greek Kalends.   Nevertheless,
some advance towards rational theories of morals is
being made, and in this matter Herbert Spencer, in
his *Data of Ethics*, and Huxley, in more fugitive form,
have done much.   That death is not the penalty of sin
is proved by the indisputable evidence of the fossil-
yielding rocks; but wrong-doing is still held to be an
infraction of divine law, and to involve pains and
penalties in a future state.   As opposed to this, wrong-
doing is held, under the doctrine of evolution, to be
an infraction of human law.

The actions we call sinful are as much the consequence of
the order of nature as those we call virtuous.   They are all
part and parcel of the struggle for existence through which
all living things have passed, and they have become sins
because man alone seeks a higher life in voluntary association.[1]

We are in ignorance alike as to the beginnings of
[1] II. 282.

consciousness and the beginnings of ethics. But as
we trace the evolution of the nervous system from
irritability in the lowest organisms to sensibility in its
ever-increasing complexity, till the higher we ascend the
more acute do we find the feelings associated with pain
and pleasure, so it is permissible to trace the germs of
morality, which lie in sympathy, among the social
animals. Into the marvels of their organisation, perhaps more astounding among invertebrates, as ants and
bees, than among the higher gregarious mammals, there
is neither need nor space to enter here; enough that
the links in the chain of psychical life of man and the
creatures beneath him are unbroken. Moreover, the
evidences as to the social bases of ethics are contained
in human history.[1] The terms "good" and "evil"
have no meaning till communal life begins. Where
there is no society there is no sin. A solitary man
on an uninhabited island can do no wrong, but when
Robinson Crusoe meets Friday, the question of be-
haviour of one to the other arises; and conduct is
ethic. Restraint on individual action begins; and the

[1] To whatever extent Mr Balfour may draw untenable inferences
from such premisses, the admission made in the new edition of his
Foundations of Belief is significant. He says that "study of evolution and modern anthropology is making us realise that the beginnings
of morality are lost among the self-preserving and race-prolonging
instincts which we share with the animal creation; that religion in
its higher forms is a development of infantine and often brutal
superstitions; and that in the pedigree of the noblest and most
subtle of our emotions are to be discerned primitive strains of
coarsest quality."

morality of the action is determined by circumstances ; hence the relativity of morals, and the origin of artificial codes which, ruled solely by conventions, make a breach of etiquette a less pardonable offence than the seduction of a woman.

Upon the general basis of ethics Huxley speaks with no uncertain sound :—

Moral duty consists in the observance of those rules of conduct which contribute to the welfare of society, and, by implication, of the individuals who compose it.

The end of society is peace and mutual protection, so that the individual may reach the fullest and highest life attainable by man. The rules of conduct by which this end is to be attained are discoverable—like the other so-called laws of Nature—by observation and experiment, and only in that way.

Some thousands of years of such experience have led to the generalisations that stealing and murder, for example, are inconsistent with the ends of society. There is no more doubt that they are so than that unsupported stones tend to fall. The man who steals or murders breaks his implied contract with society, and forfeits all protection. He becomes an outlaw, to be dealt with as any other feral creature. Criminal law indicates the ways which have proved most convenient for dealing with him.

All this would be true if men had no "moral sense" at all, just as there are rules of perspective which must be strictly observed by a draughtsman, and are quite independent of his having any artistic sense.

The moral sense is a very complex affair—dependent in part upon associations of pleasure and pain, approbation and disapprobation, formed by education in early youth, but in part also on an innate sense of moral beauty and ugliness (how originated need not be discussed), which is possessed by some people in great strength, while some are totally devoid of it—just as some children draw, or are enchanted by music while mere infants, while others do not know "Cherry Ripe" from "Rule Britannia," nor can represent the form of the simplest thing to the end of their lives.[1]

Now for this sort of people there is no reason why they should discharge any sort of moral duty, except from fear of punishment in all its grades, from mere disapprobation to hanging, and the duty of society is to see that they live under wholesome fear of such punishment, short, sharp, and decisive.

For the people with a keen innate sense of moral beauty there is no need of any other motive. What they want is knowledge of the things they may do and must leave undone, if the welfare of society is to be attained. Good people so often forget this that some of them occasionally require hanging as much as the bad.

If you ask why the moral inner sense is to be (under due limitations) obeyed, and why the few who are steered by it move the mass in whom it is weak? I can only reply by putting another question, Why do the few in whom the sense of beauty is strong — Shakespeare, Raffaele, Beethoven — carry the less endowed multitude away? But they do, and always will. People who overlook that fact attend neither to history nor to what goes on about them.

Benjamin Franklin was a shrewd, excellent, kindly man. I have a great respect for him. The force of genial common-sense respectability could no further go. George Fox was the very antipodes of all this, and yet one understands how he came to move the world of his day, and Franklin did not.

As to whether we can all fulfil the moral law, I should say hardly any of us. Some of us are utterly incapable of fulfilling its plainest dictates. As there are men born physically cripples and intellectually idiots, so there are some who are

---

[1] Cf. *Coll. Essays*, vi. p. 239.

moral cripples and idiots, and can be kept straight not even
by punishment. For these people there is nothing but
shutting-up, or extirpation.[1]

In the early stages of man's history ethics had no
connection with theology.

With the advance of civilisation, and the growth of
cities and of nations by the coalescence of families and of
tribes, the rules which constitute the common foundation
of morality and of law become more numerous and complicated, and the temptations to break or evade many of
them stronger. In the absence of a clear apprehension
of the natural sanctions of these rules, a supernatural
sanction was assumed ; and imagination supplied the
motives which reason was supposed to be incompetent to
furnish. Religion, at first independent of morality, gradually took morality under its protection ; and the super-
naturalists have ever since tried to persuade mankind that
the existence of ethics is bound up with that of supernaturalism.[2]

It has been so much the worse for both. For if the
ethical code is low, the conception of the god who is
assumed to be its author suffers as the ethical ideal
advances ; and if the ethics are made dependent upon
a theology which becomes discredited, they stand or
fall with it. Doubtless, in rude and turbulent ages,
no small gain accrued through the association of a
humane code of conduct with supernatural dogmas, but
the engine of aggrandisement which this put into the
hands of sacerdotalism rendered the divorce imperative
as society advanced.

[1] II. 305, 306.   [2] *Coll. Essays*, v. p. 53, and cf. iv. p. 361,

Theological apologists who insist that morality will vanish if their dogmas are exploded, would do well to consider the fact that, in the matter of intellectual veracity, science is already a long way ahead of the Churches ; and that, in this particular, it is exerting an educational influence on mankind of which the Churches have shown themselves utterly incapable.[1]

Moreover, a code of morals resting on the assumption of supernatural authority seeks to enforce its decrees by threats of penalties inflicted under supernatural conditions, threats which are found to be feebly operative upon conduct. Discarding such assumption, the evolutionist appeals to more tangible motives ; to the fact that actions make or mar other lives, and retard or quicken the progress of mankind. He shows that the law of causation operates in the moral sphere, and that the consequences of our deeds are immediate, or, in large degree, measurable. The brevity of life thus becomes a sharper spur to duty, and the ultimate destiny of the race, as predicted by science, a stimulus to smooth its career.

It may, Huxley says,

be well to remember that the highest level of moral aspiration recorded in history was reached by a few ancient Jews — Micah, Isaiah, and the rest—who took no count whatever of what might or might not happen to them after death. It is not obvious to me why the same point should not by-and-by be reached by the Gentiles.[2]

This all-important question of social ethics filled much

[1] *Coll. Essays*, v. p. 142.   [2] II. 304.

R

of his thought from the old Rotherhithe days to the
end. It inspired the noble Romanes Lecture, concerning which he wrote to the founder, " Of course I
will keep absolutely clear of theology. But I have long
had fermenting in my head some notions about the
relations of ethics and evolution (or rather the absence
of such as are commonly supposed) which, I think, will
be interesting to such an audience as I may expect."[1]
The discourse provoked much controversy and even
more misunderstanding, causing Huxley regret that he
did not remember Faraday's useful precept to lecturers,
to assume that even " select and cultivated " listeners
knew nothing whatever of the subject.[2]

Some of Huxley's audience took the lecture as a
senile recantation of the faith as it is in Evolution;
while, since there is no logical halting-point between
Agnosticism and Catholicism, the late Professor St
George Mivart, whose fate it was to be excommunicated
by his Church because he refused to sign a monstrous
assent to everything in the Bible, welcomed the lecture
as indicating a possible reconciliation of Huxley with the
Vatican.[3]

Ethics and Evolution, to the preparation of which
Huxley gave the utmost care, and which will abide as
a masterpiece of sonorous English prose, was the ampli-
fication of arguments used by him in various previous
utterances. It was an effort, he explained to more than

[1] II. 350.   [2] *Coll. Essays*, ix. p. vii.
[3] *Nineteenth Century*, Aug. 1893, p. 210.

one correspondent, " to put the Christian doctrine, that
Satan is the Prince of this world, upon a scientific
foundation " !   The main thesis was briefly sketched
in an essay, published five years previously (in 1888),
on the " Struggle for Existence in Human Society," and
appropriately reprinted in the volume containing the
Romanes Lecture.

In the strict sense of the word " nature," it denotes the sum
of the phenomenal world, of that which has been, and is, and
will be ; and society, like art, is therefore a part of nature.
But it is convenient to distinguish those parts of nature in
which man plays the part of immediate cause, as something
apart; and, therefore, society, like art, is usefully to be considered as distinct from nature.   It is the more desirable,
and even necessary, to make this distinction, since society
differs from nature in having a definite moral object ; whence
it comes about that the course shaped by the ethical man—
the member of society or citizen—necessarily runs counter to
that which the non-ethical man — the primitive savage, or
man as a mere member of the animal kingdom—tends to
adopt.   The latter fights out the struggle for existence to the
bitter end, like any other animal ; the former devotes his
best energies to the object of setting limits to the struggle.
. . . The ideal of the ethical man is to limit his freedom of
action to a sphere in which he does not interfere with the
freedom of others ; he seeks the common weal as much as
his own, and indeed, as an essential part of his own welfare.
Peace is both end and means with him ; and he founds his
life on a more or less complete self-restraint, which is the
negation of the unlimited struggle for existence.   He tries to
escape from his place in the animal kingdom, founded on
the free development of the principle of non-moral evolution,
and to establish a kingdom of Man, governed solely upon the

principle of moral evolution. For society not only has a moral end, but, in its perfection, social life is embodied morality.[1]

In 1890 Huxley writes : " Of moral purpose I see no trace in Nature. That is an article of exclusively human manufacture—and very much to our credit.[2] George Meredith gives rhythmic expression to that view in his great poem on man's relation to Nature :—

> " He may entreat, aspire,
> He may despair, and she has never heed ;
> She drinking his warm sweat will soothe his need,
> Not his desire." [3]

To the many the argument seemed paradoxical, for how, it was asked, could ethical nature, as the offspring of cosmic nature, be at enmity with it ? In a Prolegomena,[4] which is longer than the lecture, Huxley contended that the seeming paradox is a truth.

Taking, as an example, the ground on which his house was built, he shows how the industry of man has converted a patch of weed-choked, economically unproductive soil into a fruitful garden, and how, if the skill and labour by which this has been done are withdrawn, nature, whose action never pauses, will reassert sway, and convert the place into a wilderness. The garden is a work of art, as is the house which stands in it ; as is everything that man has produced. And the effect of

---

[1] *Coll. Essays*, ix. pp. 202, 205. [2] II. 268.
[3] *Poems and Lyrics of the Joy of Earth*, p. 119.
[4] *Coll. Essays*, ix. pp. 1-45.

all that he does is to oppose, and, for a time, arrest, the cosmic process, limiting the area of ceaseless struggle and competition. Applying this to human society, which, "at its origin, was as much a product of organic necessity as that of the bees," the "ape and tiger" instincts are found dominant. It was based on selfishness. The race was to the swift, and the battle to the strong. Even then, however, in the earliest grouping of a few families into clans or gentes, the blood-tie, whose source is in the parent, engendered a sympathy which assured unity, and, therefore, some restraint on individual assertion. For sympathy is the germ-plasm of ethics. Knowledge, the only begetter of a wider sympathy, breaks down tribal divisions, and with the obvious advantage which co-operation secures, enlarges the narrow borders of primitive altruism, limits the area of conflict, and mitigates the horrors of a state of warfare which, at the outset, was chronic. But the cosmic process is checked only locally and intermittently. To this the state of mankind, after thousands of years of advance from the feral state, witnesses, since only in the minority of all who have ever lived has that advance been made, and even among these there needs small provocation to arouse the lightly sleeping "tiger." Hence, wherever self-restraint is practised, there is checking of the cosmic process of bitter struggle by the ethical, defined by Huxley as the "evolution of the feelings out of which the primitive bonds of human society are so largely forged into the organised and personified sympathy we call conscience." [1]   Then comes into play the golden rule of Jesus, of Confucius, and of Plato : " May I do to others as I would that they should do to me." [2]

If the ethical process is not a part of the cosmical process, it must have been imported, and is therefore to be referred to supernatural intervention.   But as opposing one action against another, it has its correspondences in man's checks upon the operation of natural selection, and in the forces at play within the cosmos itself.   For the equilibrium towards which all things in the universe are tending is arrested by the activity of the conflicting agencies of repulsion and attraction ; and in all the mechanical means whereby human life is strengthened and lengthened, the action of natural selection is retarded.   And, as already observed, the rudiments of ethics are found deep down in the animal world. " Among birds and mammals societies are formed of which the bond in many cases seems to be purely psychological—that is to say, it appears to depend upon the liking of the individuals for one another's company. Love and fear come into play, and enforce a greater or less renunciation of self-will." [3]

But " the theory of evolution encourages no millennial anticipations."   As the story of the formation and dissolution of the solar system and kindred aggregations is but a chapter in a history which had no beginning and

---

[1] *Coll. Essays*, ix. p. 30.   [2] *Laws*, xi. 913 (Jowett's trans.)
[3] *Coll. Essays*, ix. p. 115.

will have no end, so life as a whole upon this globe is
but a brief chapter of that history, and the life of man a
momentary episode in the chapter.

Neither optimist nor pessimist in a world which he
confessed was "a hopeless riddle,"[1] Huxley was no
dweller at ease in a scientific Zion. As in the intellectual sphere he had exercised the spirit of inquiry by
which alone advance in knowledge is possible, so in the
moral sphere he gave expression to the spirit of dis-
content by which alone amelioration is possible.

There are [he said] two things I really care about—one
is the progress of scientific thought, and the other is the
bettering of the condition of the masses of the people by
bettering them in the way of lifting themselves out of the
misery which has hitherto been the lot of the majority of
them. Posthumous fame is not particularly attractive to
me, but, if I am to be remembered at all, I would rather
it should be as "a man who did his best to help the
people" than by any other title.

Even the best of modern civilisations appears to me to
exhibit a condition of mankind which neither embodies
any worthy ideal nor even possesses the merit of stability.
I do not hesitate to express my opinion that, if there is no
hope of a large improvement of the condition of the greater
part of the human family; if it is true that the increase of
knowledge, the winning of a greater dominion over Nature
which is its consequence, and the wealth which follows
on that dominion, are to make no difference in the extent
and the intensity of Want, with its concomitant physical
and moral degradation, among the masses of the people, I
should hail the advent of some kindly comet, which would
sweep the whole affair away, as a desirable consummation.

---

[1] II. 134.

What profits it to the human Prometheus that he has stolen the fire of heaven to be his servant, and that the spirits of the earth and the air obey him, if the vulture of pauperism is eternally to tear his very vitals and keep him on the brink of destruction ?[1]

Moved by these gloomy facts to "work while it is yet day," Huxley found little, save for adverse criticism, in the social reform schemes which "have infested political thought for centuries." He had no belief in "leaders" and "saviours" of society, or in the "fanatical individualism of our time which attempts to apply the analogy of cosmic nature to society, and seriously debates whether the members of a community are justified in using their strength to constrain one of their number to contribute his share to the maintenance of it, or even to prevent him from doing his best to destroy it,"[2] and which would limit the exercise of State rights to the protection of its subjects from aggression.[3] Here, once more, he had stirred up a hornet's nest of criticism from various quarters, the argument often taking the usual form of expletives. But, as he reminded his opponents, his interest in these questions "did not begin the day before yesterday"; reflection and observation had only deepened conviction, and the later essays on Government, Capital, and the Struggle for Existence, emphasised the position which he had taken up a quarter of a century earlier. Now, as then, he went to the heart of the matter in insisting on the fundamental im-

[1] *Coll. Essays*, i. p. 423 ; and cf. v. p. 256.
[2] *Coll. Essays*, ix. p. 83.   [3] *Ib.*, i. p. 258.

portance of dealing with the population question, since with short commons and lack of elbow-room there was quick shunting of the ethical process.

For the effort of ethical man to work towards a moral end by no means abolished, perhaps hardly modified, the deep-seated organic impulses which impel the natural man to follow his non-moral course. One of the most essential conditions, if not the chief cause, of the struggle for exist- ence, is the tendency to multiply without limit, which man shares with all living things. It is notable that "increase and multiply" is a commandment traditionally much older than the ten ; and that it is, perhaps, the only one which has been spontaneously and *ex animo* obeyed by the great majority of the human race. But, in civilised society, the inevitable result of such obedience is the re-establishment, in all its intensity, of that struggle for existence—the war of each against all—the mitigation or abolition of which was the chief end of social organisation.[1]

"There is no discharge in that war," and the struggle has rather increased in force than lessened since Huxley wrote these words. Competition becomes sharper ; and the cry for protection is a return to the narrow ethics of the tribe. The community that trusts to old repute and disdains new methods, and that artificially reduces each member of its industrial classes to a common level, will be worsted in a battle where the wounded receive no quarter, and where starvation is the penalty of surrender. There survives in many parts of the globe, notably in thickly-peopled China, the practice of partly meeting the difficulty of excess of population over means of sub-

[1] *Coll. Essays,* ix. p. 205.

sistence by infanticide; while in former days, all the world over, the ravages wrought by famine, war, and pestilence were unchecked. But the progress of private and public morality has steadily tended to remove the effects of those scourges, and the finer spirits of the race dream of a society where no man shall die of hunger, and no family mourn a member slain in battle; when the Golden Age of ancient legend shall be fulfilled on the earth.

Dealing with these islands, Huxley admits the justice of the "insolent reproach" cast by Buonaparte. On a soil which can feed less than half the population, we are compelled to be "a nation of shopkeepers." The shop-keeping implies buying and selling, and if the goods offered are inferior to those of competitors, a ruinous reduction in exports will follow, leaving a large propor-tion of the population, whose only salvation is by work, with nothing to eat. A further condition must be social stability. There must be healthy homes, a cultivation of thrift, the attainment of a fair standard of material comfort, for where *la misère* reigns there is inefficiency and handicapping of the worker. And in remarking upon the absence of these conditions in many quarters of great industrial centres from London downwards, Huxley drives home the fact that here, suspending their differences, "natural science and religious enthusiasm" may work in concord towards one aim. He passes from the importance of State-endowed education, into which no theology shall intrude, to technical training, the cost of which he suggests should be borne by the districts benefited by it.   But that is a detail, the important thing being to catch the "small percentage of the population which is born with that most excellent quality, a desire for excellence, or with special aptitude of some sort or another, and turn them to account for the good of society," whose highest aim should be the making of men, not of millionaires; the development of character, not the equation of "success" with the "accumulation of cash."   "For the increase of wealth —that is, of the means of comfort—is not, necessarily, good in itself; everything depends on the way in which the wealth is distributed and its effect on the moral character of the nation."[1]

No man can say where they will crop up; like their opposites, the fools and the knaves, they appear sometimes in the palace and sometimes in the hovel; but the great thing to be aimed at—I was almost going to say, the most important end of all social arrangements—is to keep these glorious sports of Nature from being either corrupted by luxury or starved by poverty, and to put them into the position in which they can do the work for which they are specially fitted.[2]

Throughout the papers on social subjects which fill portions of the first, third, and ninth volumes of the *Collected Essays*, criticism is followed by definite suggestion.   And so it was with all matters, both practical and speculative, with which he dealt; the

---

[1] *Letters from John Chinaman*, p. 27.
[2] *Coll. Essays*, ix. p. 210.

order of his mind was architectonic. To regard Huxley as a compound of Boanerges and Iconoclast is to show entire misapprehension of the aims which inspired his labours. In Biology his discovery of the structure of the Medusæ laid the foundations of modern zoology; his theory of the origin of the skull gave a firm basis to vertebrate morphology; and his luminous exposition of the pedigree of man imported order where confusion had reigned. In the more important matter of Education he formulated principles whose adoption would bring out the best that is in every scholar, and inspire him with love of whatever "is of good report"; while his invention of the laboratory system of zoological teaching has been adopted with the best results in every school and university of repute. In Theology he separated the accidental elements from the essential, leaving as residuum a religion that, co-ordinated with the needs and aspirations of human nature, would find its highest motive and its permanency in an ethic based on sympathy.

NOTE ON THE DOCTRINE OF THE UNKNOWABLE.

SINCE the passing of the foregoing pages through the press, the following extracts from letters from Huxley to Mr F. C. Gould, written in 1889, have appeared in the *Literary Guide* of January 1902. They are an interesting addition to the remarks quoted on page 125 :—

As between Mr Spencer and myself, the question is not one of "a dividing line," but of an entire and complete divergence as soon as we leave the foundations laid by Hume, Kant, and Hamilton, who are *my* philosophical forefathers. To my mind, the "Absolute" philosophies were finally knocked on the head by Hamilton ; and the "Unknowable," in Mr Spencer's sense, is merely the Absolute *redivivus*, a sort of ghost of an extinct philosophy, the name of a negation hocus-pocussed into a sham thing. If I am to talk about that of which I have no knowledge at all, I prefer the good old word *God*, about which there is no scientific pretence.

· · · · · · · · ·

I have long been aware of the manner in which my views have been confounded with those of Mr Spencer, though no one was more fully aware of our divergence than the latter. Perhaps I have done wrongly in letting the thing slide so long, but I was anxious to avoid a breach with an old

friend. . . . Whether the Unknowable or any other Nou-
menon exists or does not exist, I am quite clear I have no
knowledge either way. So with respect to whether there is
anything behind Force or not, I am ignorant ; I neither
affirm nor deny. The tendency of the human mind to idolatry is so strong that, *faute de mieux*, it falls down and
worships negative abstractions, as much the creation of the
mind as the stone idol of the hands. The one object of the
Agnostic (in the true sense) is to knock this tendency on the
head whenever or wherever it shows itself. Our physical
science is full of it.

INDEX.

THE END

PRINTED BY WILLIAM BLACKWOOD AND SONS.

PERIODS OF EUROPEAN LITERATURE.

A COMPLETE AND CONTINUOUS HISTORY OF THE SUBJECT.

Edited by PROFESSOR SAINTSBURY.

In 12 crown 8vo vols., each 5s. net.

I. THE DARK AGES. By Prof. W. P. KER.
II. THE FLOURISHING OF ROMANCE AND THE RISE OF ALLEGORY. (12TH AND 13TH CENTURIES.) By GEORGE SAINTSBURY, M.A., Hon. LL.D. Aberdeen, Professor of Rhetoric and English Literature in Edinburgh University.
III. THE FOURTEENTH CENTURY. By F. J. SNELL.
IV. THE TRANSITION PERIOD. By G. GREGORY SMITH.
V. THE EARLIER RENAISSANCE. By The EDITOR.
VI. THE LATER RENAISSANCE. By DAVID HANNAY.
VII. THE FIRST HALF OF THE SEVENTEENTH CENTURY. By Prof. H. J. C. GRIERSON.
VIII. THE AUGUSTAN AGES. By PROFESSOR ELTON.
IX. THE MID-EIGHTEENTH CENTURY. By J. H. MILLAR.
X. THE ROMANTIC REVOLT. By Prof. C. E. VAUGHAN.
[In preparation.
XI. THE ROMANTIC TRIUMPH. By T. S. OMOND.
XII. THE LATER NINETEENTH CENTURY. By The EDITOR.
[In preparation.

PHILOSOPHICAL CLASSICS
FOR ENGLISH READERS.

Edited by PROFESSOR KNIGHT, LL.D.

Price 1s. each.

Descartes. Prof. MAHAFFY.
Butler. Rev. W. L. COLLINS.
Berkeley. Prof. CAMPBELL FRASER.
Fichte. Prof. ADAMSON.
Kant. Prof. WALLACE.
Hamilton. Prof. VEITCH.
Hegel. The MASTER OF BALLIOL.
Leibniz. JOHN THEODORE MERZ.

Vico. Prof. FLINT.
Hobbes. Prof. CROOM ROBERTSON.
Hume. Prof. KNIGHT.
Spinoza. Principal CAIRD.
Bacon: PART I. Prof. NICHOL.
Bacon: PART II. Prof. NICHOL.
Locke. Prof. CAMPBELL FRASER.

WILLIAM BLACKWOOD & SONS, EDINBURGH AND LONDON.

FOREIGN CLASSICS

FOR ENGLISH READERS.

Edited by MRS OLIPHANT.

Limp cloth, price 1s. each.

Dante. The EDITOR.
Voltaire. General Sir E. B. HAMLEY, K.C.B.
Pascal. Principal TULLOCH.
Petrarch. HENRY REEVE, C.B.
Goethe. A. HAYWARD, Q.C.
Molière. The EDITOR and F. TARVER, M.A.
Montaigne. Rev. W. L. COLLINS.
Rabelais. Sir WALTER BESANT.
Calderon. E. J. HASELL.
Saint Simon. C. W. COLLINS.
Cervantes. The EDITOR.

Corneille and Racine. HENRY M. TROLLOPE.
Madame de Sévigné. Miss THACKERAY.
La Fontaine and other French Fabulists. Rev. W. LUCAS COLLINS, M.A.
Schiller. JAMES SIME, M.A.
Tasso. E. J. HASELL.
Rousseau. HENRY GREY GRAHAM.
Alfred de Musset. C. F. OLIPHANT.

ANCIENT CLASSICS

FOR ENGLISH READERS.

Edited by the REV. W. LUCAS COLLINS, M.A.

Limp cloth, price 1s. each.

Homer: Iliad. The EDITOR.
Homer: Odyssey. The EDITOR.
Herodotus. G. C. SWAYNE.
Cæsar. ANTHONY TROLLOPE.
Virgil. The EDITOR.
Horace. Sir THEODORE MARTIN.
Æschylus. Bishop COPLESTONE.
Xenophon. Sir ALEX. GRANT.
Cicero. The EDITOR.
Sophocles. C. W. COLLINS.
Pliny. Rev. A. CHURCH and W. J. BRODRIBB.
Euripides. W. B. DONNE.
Juvenal. E. WALFORD.
Aristophanes. The EDITOR.
Hesiod and Theognis. J. DAVIES.

Plautus and Terence. The EDITOR.
Tacitus. W. B. DONNE.
Lucian. The EDITOR.
Plato. C. W. COLLINS.
Greek Anthology. Lord NEAVES.
Livy. The EDITOR.
Ovid. Rev. A. CHURCH.
Catullus, Tibullus, and Propertius. J. DAVIES.
Demosthenes. W. J. BRODRIBB.
Aristotle. Sir ALEX. GRANT.
Thucydides. The EDITOR.
Lucretius. W. H. MALLOCK.
Pindar. Rev. F. D. MORICE.

WILLIAM BLACKWOOD & SONS, EDINBURGH AND LONDON.